'This publication is a must read guide for parents, clinicians and medical personnel. It is a radical reminder for us to consider the whole family in time of loss and a developmental and frank approach to telling the truth to children about death. It opens a new practice for creative arts therapists and child life specialists and argues the case for ICU and hospital administrators to prepare for and accommodate children and families facing the death of their loved one.'

Alice Forrester, *PhD, CEO, Clifford Beers Community Health Partners*

'This book is a heartfelt invitation to embrace the paradox of death within holistic, family-centered care. With unwavering courage, Stephanie Omens demystifies the difficult terrain of illness and loss, offering a transformative perspective. Each of her stories encourages us to confront uncomfortable cultural truths surrounding grief and find a compassionate and honest path forward that centers the experience of children. This book is a must-read for anyone committed to caring for grieving families.'

Nisha Sajnani, *PhD, RDT-BCT, Director: Graduate Program in Drama Therapy, New York University; Founder: Arts & Health @ NYU; Director: Theatre & Health Lab; Chair: Creative Arts Therapies Consortium; Faculty: Educational Theatre & Rehabilitation Science PhD Programs; Editor: Drama Therapy Review*

'Dramatherapy and the Bereaved Child is an extraordinary book revealing one of the hardest encounters a young person can make—with death. Stephanie Omens guides such encounters with grace, humility, dignity, depth of feeling and wisdom. Her deeply affecting clinical narratives offer a lens into how, why, when and where creative approaches of dramatherapy best serve the lives of grieving children and their families. These stories are indelible and should be required reading for all clinicians and other humans who will inevitably experience the same encounter.'

Robert Landy, *PhD, RDT-BCT, LCAT, Professor Emeritus, Founding Director, Drama Therapy Program, New York University*

Dramatherapy and the Bereaved Child

This book addresses the needs of children experiencing the hospitalization or death of a caregiver or loved one to comprehend and cope with tragedy with the assistance creative non-fictions and dramatic play.

Based on the author's two-decade-long clinical practice and an extensive career working with bereaved children and their families as a dramatherapist and child life practitioner, this book demonstrates how storytelling and dramatherapy can be used to tell the truth to children in these difficult circumstances. Through vivid and candid case examples, the author demonstrates the developmentally normative, dramatic, and psychotherapeutic principles that inform her work. She shares stories for children that are carefully constructed to help children understand the truth of what they are facing rather than shielding them from reality. Attuned to the children's direct experience, these stories take care to respect the culture and context of the death, and the histories of the people involved.

The book, accessibly written, will provide guidance, insight, and comfort for professionals, clinicians, and grieving children and their families. Additional reader resources can be found at www.routledge.com/9780367461041 under "Support Material".

Stephanie Omens is a Licensed Creative Arts Therapist, Mental Health Counselor, Registered Drama Therapist, Board Certified, and Certified Child Life Specialist in private practice in New York and New Jersey. She is an adjunct instructor at New York University and Lesley University. Further resources, contact details and information about Stephanie can be found here: https://nowhitelies.com/

Dramatherapy: approaches, relationships, critical ideas

Series Editor: Professor Anna Seymour

This series brings together leading practitioners and researchers in the field of Dramatherapy to explore the practices, thinking and evidence base for Dramatherapy.

Each volume focuses on a particular aspect of Dramatherapy practice, its application with a specific client group, an exploration of a particular methodology or approach or the relationship between Dramatherapy and related field(s) of practice, all informed by ongoing critical analysis of existing and emergent theoretical ideas.

In each case the aim is to develop the knowledge base of Dramatherapy as a unique discipline, whilst contextualising and acknowledging its relationship with others arts and therapeutic practices.

As such the series will produce different kinds of books to encompass a spectrum of readers from trainee Dramatherapists and arts practitioners to academic researchers engaged in multidisciplinary enquiry.

The field of Dramatherapy is expanding internationally and this series aims to respond to emergent clinical and critical needs within practice based and academic settings. These settings are increasingly diverse serving complex needs and demand dynamic and incisive literature to support clinical intervention and as resources for critique.

In this series:

Dramatherapy and Learning Disabilities: Developing Emotional Growth, Autonomy and Self-Worth
Edited by Helen Milward and Anna Seymour

Dramatherapy and Recovery: The CoActive Therapeutic Theatre Model and Manual
By Laura L. Wood and Dave Mowers

Dramatherapy and the Bereaved Child: Telling the Truth to Children During Difficult Times
By Stephanie Omens

For a full list of titles in this series, please visit: https://www.routledge.com/mentalhealth/series/DRAMA

Dramatherapy and the Bereaved Child

Telling the Truth to Children during Difficult Times

Stephanie Omens

Routledge
Taylor & Francis Group

LONDON AND NEW YORK

First published 2024
by Routledge
4 Park Square, Milton Park, Abingdon, Oxon OX14 4RN

and by Routledge
605 Third Avenue, New York, NY 10158

Routledge is an imprint of the Taylor & Francis Group, an informa business

British Library Cataloguing-in-Publication Data
A catalogue record for this book is available from the British Library

Library of Congress Cataloging-in-Publication Data
Names: Omens, Stephanie, 1965- author.
Title: Dramatherapy and the bereaved child : telling the truth to children during difficult times / Stephanie Omens.
Description: Abingdon, Oxon ; New York, NY : Routledge, 2024. |
Series: Dramatherapy: approaches, relationships, critical ideas |
Identifiers: LCCN 2023047563 (print) | LCCN 2023047564 (ebook) | ISBN 9780367461058 (hbk) | ISBN 9780367461041 (pbk) | ISBN 9781003026938 (ebk)
Subjects: LCSH: Bereavement in children. | Families--Psychological aspects.
Classification: LCC BF723.G75 O56 2024 (print) | LCC BF723.G75 (ebook) | DDC 155.9/37083--dc23/eng/20231220
LC record available at https://lccn.loc.gov/2023047563
LC ebook record available at https://lccn.loc.gov/2023047564

ISBN: 978-0-367-46105-8 (hbk)
ISBN: 978-0-367-46104-1 (pbk)
ISBN: 978-1-003-02693-8 (ebk)

DOI: 10.4324/9781003026938

Typeset in Calibri
by MPS Limited, Dehradun

Additional reader resources can be found online as Support Material
www.routledge.com/9780367461041

This book is dedicated to my daughter Emma, you are a wish come true.

And in loving memory of my mother

1944–1991

Contents

Foreword

NoWhiteLies

David Read Johnson

There are some people capable of rushing into a burning building to put out a fire. There are some who can run into battle to protect their country. There are those who arrive at a motor vehicle accident on the highway and others who can receive the injured in an emergency department. This book is about those—a precious few—who are capable of entering the quiet, time-altered hospital room and being with children who are about to die or whose parent is about to die, amidst the tubes and murmuring machines, the smells, and relentless pain.

Stephanie Omens weds dramatherapy, child life, and bereavement in stories of unbearable grief. Unlike firefighters, soldiers, or ER nurses, she faces no emergency that can compel action; there is only the elephantine truth of what is happening there. What she finds surrounding these catastrophes is a cloud of denial, euphemism, distraction, and—at its heart—lies. Lies that any of us would embrace if confronted with this same situation.

More than the therapeutic treatment of bereavement, this book is about ethics. What we are told from page one through to the end is that lying, for whatever motivation, is harmful to the child. Not often since Immanuel Kant, in his moral philosophy of the categorical imperative, has such a stark position been taken. In his essay, "On the supposed right to tell lies from benevolent motives," written in 1795, he provides Omens with solid ground for her message: that children benefit from the truth—even if it concerns their own or their parents' death—because it is impossible to live life based on false foundations, even if that life is about to end. That Kant's position has stirred up opposition (for over 200 years) will make sense to the readers of Omens' powerful book, as we are presented with the sheer terror of telling a child that their parent will not make it. That someone, knowledgeable, kind, and calm, can be there for that child in that Moment, with that Fact, is the subject of the stories and concepts that Omens gifts us.

Like trauma, death, and illness evoke fear, shame, and horror, followed promptly by avoidance, denial, isolation, and numbing. This pernicious combination produces the symptoms of psychiatric disease and its associated suffering, but more importantly, it interferes with the natural process of grieving, which relies on the encounter with truth. Mourning cannot proceed without access to the truth. This is the purpose of viewing the body at a wake: one sees the body and feels nothing, then shortly one is out in the hall laughing at a humorous memory, and then one turns a random corner and bursts out crying: loss takes time and space to metabolize, as the stories in this book illustrate with so much care.

At the basis of Ms. Omens' method, built on compassion, courage, and equanimity, is her application of dramatherapy. There is a reason for this, for theatre is a sophisticated way of telling the truth. On its surface, theatre is a lie; pretending to be something we are not, to play a role, to imagine a scene, to move our hand like it is a crocodile, is a departure from reality. However, unlike a lie, which seeks to hide itself as a lie (for why lie and then wink?), theatre is a lie that seeks to reveal itself as a lie and therefore is honest. We go to the theatre or watch a movie to see things that are not real while knowing that they are not real, and in so doing (strangely), they reveal to us truths about the human adventure. The bitterness of the fact of dying is mixed in with the playful joys and sideways smiles of imaginary worlds. Such magical acts are documented in this book, page after page.

Being present in these waiting rooms just before the end, without fear or anxious reassurance, comes to Ms. Omens from many sources: her temperament, her training, and indeed, her own experience with absence. She is well-prepared. The result for the reader is having multiple moments throughout the book of gasping for breath, of drowning in awe, as the stories of these families unfold. One concludes, I believe, that there are times for angels: as we hear how the parents leave their dead child in Ms. Omens' warm arms after saying their goodbyes, we become witnesses to what angels can do.

Stephanie Omens has written a book that is, simply, incredible.

David Read Johnson, PhD, RDT-BCT, is a drama therapist and clinical psychologist; co-director, Post Traumatic Stress Center, New Haven, CT; chief executive officer, The Miss Kendra Program; and director, Institute of Developmental Transformations. He is the co-author of Principles and Techniques in Trauma-Centered Psychotherapy and the co-editor of Current Approaches in Drama Therapy. He has published extensively on trauma, drama therapy, and the creative arts therapies.

Preface

This is a book about working with stories to help children live through the painful experience of bereavement.

The "made up" stories in this book are carefully constructed to enable children to be with the truth of what they are facing rather than, as is often the case, be shielded from the reality of what is happening. This attitude is usually based on the mistaken idea that it would be "kinder" not to tell the truth or that children are "not able to cope with" the reality of loss.

Thus children are often told lies through fantastical stories. Although it might be done with the best of intentions, this book argues that by adopting such an approach, children can be left with confusion or other potentially damaging effects. By telling stories that are attuned to the children's direct experience and taking care to respect the culture and context of the death and the histories of the people involved, I share different ways of managing these painful events.

This is not a theoretical book, though it is grounded in sound theoretical principles which underpin my clinical thinking and extensive experience in clinical practice. I will introduce these theoretical ideas through reflecting on the reasoning and structuring of clinical interventions.

The book is interspersed with accounts of family bereavement based on composite characters and situations drawn from real-life clinical work. This enables the stories of people I have worked with to be anonymized and their identities to be protected. Each individual has given permission for their story to be told, trusting that ethical principles of faithful retelling will be used. Included as well are several contributions from families I have worked with who reflected on their experiences and the effect of dramatherapy on their journeys.

Thus, I introduce different kinds of stories, from a few lines which capture intense moments to more extended examples which are offered in the manner of case studies. There are also excerpts from books that I specifically wrote for individual children which use images and metaphors to help them deal with the difficult circumstances of death. These stories are "truthful" fictions which are designed, as noted earlier, to correspond to the child's actual lived experience.

Throughout the book, readers need to be aware that they will, through empathizing and even identifying with its contents, enter sad and painful memories. Readers are urged to take care and recognize that while these experiences are tough to manage and "be with," death is an essential part of life. It's not my intention to "harm" the reader with the sorrow. I bear no responsibility for these tragedies. These events are no one's fault, and no one could prevent the sadness of the children's experiences—but I could support and help them tolerate the sorrow in the ways I outline. I ask the reader to support the children whose stories are shared by witnessing and tolerating their lived experience and sorrow. In doing so, perhaps we can expand *our* tolerance to sit with the discomfort.

In the text, readers will note that stories which enter into these lived experiences are italicized, with longer stories denoted at the beginning by a symbol:

Finally, it is important to acknowledge that the motivation to commit to doing this work is deeply embedded in my own experience of loss and bereavement as a child. I share my own story with readers to demonstrate how the capacity to be with grief and loss can, over many years, become a source of strength and creativity which in my case was transformed into my becoming a therapist.

Acknowledgements

The following pages would not have been possible without the support of many very important people in my life. My editor, Anna Seymour, for your encouragement and unwavering belief in me and this project. Thank you.

My eternal gratitude to Kat Lee, without whom this book would not otherwise have been written. You played many roles during this process, seamlessly shifting between them and holding my hand, at times pulling me by the hand to completion. Thank you for all the words you helped me find, from cover to cover, my eternal gratitude.

I am grateful to my loving family for their support and to my dearest friends, Maria Hodermarska, David Read Johnson, Adam Reynolds, Alice Forester, Nisha Sajnani, Erika Leewenburgh, Katie Demarko, Edward Rabinowitz, Auntie Donna, and Uncle Chuck, to Jordan, Susan, Josh, Allie, Zach, and many of the Good Omens in my life.

I wish to acknowledge my chosen family, I am so grateful for your love and support. And to the numerous children and families whose stories I am honoured to tell here. In loving memory of those whose lives will never be forgotten.

Chapter 1

Introduction

1.1 Nikky and Kenny's Story

I met Sharon for the first time during one of her initial oncology appointments. She wanted to know how to talk to her young children about her recent breast cancer diagnosis, her upcoming reconstruction surgery, and how chemotherapy would affect her. I introduced myself to Sharon and her husband in an exam room after her appointment with the doctor. She showed me photos of her children, 2-year-old Kenny and 4-year-old Nikky, and spoke about them to me. "They look just like you," I said. They had light hair and blue eyes, just like their mother. In the photo, the family stood in front of a Disney castle, looking happy and smiling. That was before their world changed—before Sharon discovered a small lump in her breast. Before the mammograms, the biopsy, and the shocking diagnosis: breast cancer. Sharon was 35 years old.

Sharon and her husband Paul talked about their children, how bright and curious they were. She wanted to help them understand why she was going to the doctor's office so frequently and find words to explain cancer to them. She told me that she had not said anything to them, avoiding their questions about the changes in their routine and the bruises and Band-Aids on her arms from the frequent blood draws. No longer being able to pick them up from school felt unthinkable. "It never happens," she said, "We never leave them with sitters, and we've never slept away from the kids." Sharon instinctively felt she needed a way to speak with Nikky and Kenny about her illness. She wanted them to understand all the changes they were witnessing, as well as the changes they would see in the coming weeks and months of her treatment.

I asked questions about the children, about Sharon's diagnosis, and the medical plan. The tumour was small and the oncologist's recommendations for a mastectomy and chemotherapy were largely precautionary. Sharon and Paul were very positive. I asked what they had already told Nikky and Kenny. In my assessment, it was clear that the children were experiencing stress reactions—watching their mother closely, asking many "whys"—and that

DOI: 10.4324/9781003026938-1

Sharon and Paul, while loving and present, had been omitting information and leaving their children without answers. I provided my recommendations for the children based on their ages and their parents' desire to include them in Sharon's care: to keep them informed about her illness, just as they talked to them openly and honestly about everything else in their lives. I gave them age-appropriate vocabulary and a simple structure for them to sit down and talk to Nikky and Kenny, so that both parents and children could feel secure. We created a clear plan so that they knew what to say and could anticipate their children's questions and reactions. Working with them was straightforward; I did not need to meet the children, only to meet with the parents a few times to guide them through this process. A week later, they told me that the conversation, although difficult, went much better than they had expected. Sharon was relieved to have told them. The children, she said, had understood everything through the language I provided, and were coping very well both at home and at school.

I have had thousands of these conversations, talking to countless parents and children about difficult situations. Rarely do I meet parents like Sharon who, at the outset of a new diagnosis, already want to speak with her children and talk to them openly and honestly. Attuned parents intuitively understand that their children will sense that there is something different. They value the consistency of truth-telling—not only about the easy things to discuss in their lives but also about very difficult concepts, like Sharon's cancer diagnosis and treatment. Most parents say nothing, wishing to protect their kids by their silence. Finding themselves in unthinkable situations, like in the exam room at an oncologist's office, most parents I meet with have not reached out as Sharon did. Their attempts to keep their children from harm have often included shielding them from the information. Yet when adults withhold the truth, children become more confused.

There is no preparation for these difficult conversations. Very few clinicians are experienced in this work. In addition, there are limitations on the part of the medical team. Doctors skilled in oncological treatment are not specialized in the psychosocial needs of patients' children. Psychosocial support staff, while skilled in providing for concrete social service needs, may not be aware of the developmental needs of the child in understanding their parent's potentially life-limiting illness. This is further compounded by a general discomfort about the whole conversation. When confronted by the needs of young children whose lives are affected by difficult medical situations, most parents and medical professionals I have encountered avoid the truth, speak in euphemisms, or lie. Yet they are not protecting or helping the child by keeping information from them. The non-truth—not malicious in intention, spoken in an attempt to protect the child—creates more confusion. Mistruths can increase fear, breed mistrust, and compound the child's anxiety (see Chapter 5).

I envision a procedural approach, in which the Sharons of the world are not the exception but the norm. My objective is to treat the whole family, addressing the emotional and psychosocial needs of the children of adult patients, as well as the adult patients themselves.

1.2 Who Is the Book for and Why?

This book goes to the heart of what it means to provide holistic, family-centred care. We must include children by guiding parents and professionals to support their needs. This book aims to increase understanding of the developmental and psychosocial needs of children dealing with hospitalizations or the loss of a loved one, with particular attention paid to the efficacy of dramatherapy in addressing those issues.

I am aware that this material is challenging. It is not easy to read stories about death and dying, but this is the body of my work in the hospital system. My intention is to demystify death, providing a framework to understand and talk about it. In doing so, I hope to make the subject more accessible rather than distancing ourselves by making it overly precious. This book does not shield the reader from stories about death and dying. Rather, it invites us to engage with the topic and expand our capacity to tolerate it. While it is not easy to talk to children about death, I aim to show it can be done simply.

1.2.1 For the Healthcare Provider

I wish to share a body of work that will raise awareness and broaden the meaning of patient- and family-centred care. Healthcare is siloed into special-izations, with each profession allocated to different parts of the body. Yet it is increasingly marketable for practitioners and systems to emphasize holistic approaches in the care of patients and families: integrated, developmental, and transdisciplinary care. A hospital system that creates a whole culture toward healing should include the needs of children: not only paediatric patients, but also the children of adult patients.

As trained professionals, we are ethically accountable to provide clinical competency for bereaved children within the hospital setting. Their needs, which are affected by the medical illnesses of their loved ones, are significant, yet they are often overlooked in the care team's approach to treating potentially life-limiting illnesses. From a family systems perspective, teams must address the needs of the whole family. This shifts the primary focus to include not only the patient but all family members affected by the illness, including the children whom systems often overlook.

1.2.2 For the Dramatherapist

Dramatherapy provides a pathway to renewal and insight through emotional expression and catharsis. In cases of acute, potentially life-limiting illness or active phases of death, attention to feelings is often secondary to the treatment of the body. Yet the body is not an appendage of the mind, and the mind is not disconnected from the body.

Shakespeare's notion that "All the world's a stage" suggests an integrated perspective, one that I consider as I approach families in the intensive care unit (ICU). The stage encompasses many art forms: choreography, orchestration, set design, lighting, costumes, sound, staging, actors … even intermission and refreshments. I apply these elements, the tools of stagecraft, as the principal framework for my therapeutic interventions.

In Judaism, the interpretation of the Torah is an ancient study known as *midrash*: to understand, explore, and pass down the meaning of Biblical stories. Within a family, such a passing down of stories is essential to a lineage, so that the lost life can be known and remembered, leaving a legacy behind. How will this patient's story be told? What is the trajectory of the illness and how is it narrated? What aspects of life will be remembered and how will those lived memories be honoured after life?

I aim to explore rather than to answer these questions, using theatre and the ancient art of reflection. The dramatic arts make space for the creative portrayal of stories, told and retold. The hospital room becomes the stage where the final scene is enacted and the stories collected. I ask about the ill family member to understand how that person interacted with the world. I build on these elements to create lasting memories for bereaved children.

1.2.3 For Parents

Parents protect their children from harm. We are biologically hard-wired to do this, from the moment of their conception. Our ability to protect and keep our children out of harm's way is fundamental to their survival. However, in spite of their protective intentions, parents are often misguided when seeking recommendations and support during their most vulnerable time in life: when illness enters the family home.

1.2.3.1 Even if Mommy Can't Answer Back

As the one year anniversary of his wife's death approached, I asked a widower how his 2-year-old son was doing: "Does he talk about his mother?" "Sometimes he talks to his mommy's picture," the father said, "He looks at her photo and says, 'Hi,' expecting her to talk back to him." I asked how he responded to his son in those moments. He told me he tried hard not to let his son see him crying and that, after a moment, the child would return to playing with his toys. I encouraged the father to cry openly and share stories about his wife: to talk to his son, telling him how much Mommy loves him and to validate for the child how much they both miss her. I explained that this would

be a wonderful way to keep her memory "alive" in their home; that crying and talking about her would teach his son about emotions, grief, and sadness; and that they could find a strength that comes from sharing their grief together, openly, honestly, and with vulnerability.

1.3 Background Information on the Author

I am a Licensed Creative Arts Therapist, Licensed Professional Counsellor, nationally recognized Registered Drama Therapist, and Certified Child Life Specialist. I have worked with medically compromised children in the hospital setting since 2002 and have provided adjunct instruction at New York University since 2005. I also have a private practice in New York City.

I developed NoWhiteLies (NoWhiteLies.com) to help children and their families navigate conversations about tough issues through storytelling and individualized books that explain complicated medical circumstances.

1.3.1 Using Story to Help Children Cope with Death

Children need truth and can handle the most difficult circumstances if they understand them. Story creates a shared language that a child can comprehend.

These stories begin with a conversation with the family during which I gather information.

Then I develop a narrative that supports understanding and tells the story from the child's point of view in order to be accessible. Each book is created to be placed on a shelf, where the child has access to hold it and read to themselves. The books are concrete, bound with pictures, and titled with the child's name, "A Story For … ." Even if they are unable to read the words, children memorize the visual narrative and the cadence of the story as it has been read to them.

Change is the main theme underpinning each story. The process of change is easily explainable to children through metaphors like seasonal change (See Figure 1.1).

They understand that some changes we can predict and others we cannot.

When I reflect on my personal reasons for advocating truth-telling to children during difficult times, I consider the connection to my own childhood. I have expertise in providing for the unmet needs of children, explaining difficult things, and carefully listening; however, these same things were not afforded to me as a child. I am a survivor of childhood trauma and neglect. Perhaps my focus on the needs of children is a response to the lack of consideration and care paid to me. As I look at my desire to provide children with honesty, I think about the lies told to me and my siblings as children.

My life was impacted by strong women who were not my mother but cared for me as if they were. I was saved because of their loving care and am forever grateful. My own mother's love was given with ambivalence, as she was not able

Figure 1.1 Seasonal transitions from *Everything Changes* (Omens, 2017).

to be fully present. She left my brothers and me many times. I had one choice during my childhood: to survive and to find strength because of it.

As a mother myself, I take immense joy in my relationship with my daughter as well as my niece and nephew. These relationships have brought healing. Many other factors have helped me grow: incredible therapists, family, chosen family, the dramatherapy community, and my work. Providing the clarity, honesty, and support that children deserve fulfills and maintains me. Perhaps I am called to do this work because I am keenly aware of how it feels to be raised without it.

1.4 Nikky and Kenny: Five Years Later

Five years later, Sharon called me, asking if I remembered her. She explained that sadly, after years of being healthy and cancer-free, her cancer had returned. Now metastatic, it had spread to her spine and lungs, and was quickly progressing. Sharon told me there were very few treatment options. She was devastated and asked for me to meet with her, Paul, and the children, Kenny and Nikky, now 7 and 9 years old. Sharon was determined to extend her

life, to be with her children and husband, and to do anything possible to live. I thought about how much she had put into place to support the children and Paul, not only when we had first met, but again years later. I would later reflect on how I was carrying out her wishes, even after she was no longer able to do this herself.

When the children were younger, telling the truth meant explaining to Nikky and Kenny about their mother's diagnosis of breast cancer and her expected hair loss after chemotherapy treatment. Now I would need to build upon this narrative and prepare the children for the changes in their mother's condition and eventually her death. Five years earlier, during our sessions, I had written a story for Nikky and Kenny. This explained Sharon's illness in truthful language that the children could understand. It had a strong and positive effect on them. It gave Sharon and Paul some peace of mind that they had done the right thing by telling their children the truth.

Sharon and I worked closely to write a second book. During her frequent hospitalizations, I met with Paul and the children to prepare them before and process after their visits. In the months that followed, when cancer progressed to her brain, she was not able to communicate. I spoke with Paul frequently about Nikky and Kenny, their understanding of these changes, and creative ways they could still communicate and spend meaningful time together as a family. In her final weeks, Sharon quickly declined and her interactions with her children became more difficult and limited.

In our work, we explored the love that could not be seen, yet that the children felt and knew was always there. We read a story called The Kissing Hand (Penn, 1993) about a child who is afraid to leave his mother and go off to school. The mother in the story places a kiss in the palm of her son's hand so that he can have her kiss for reassurance during times of separation. I read this story to the children and we created a therapeutic intervention to help support the love that exists, but cannot be expressed directly at this phase of Sharon's illness. I painted two mason jars, with pink and red hearts, and tied a ribbon around the top of each jar. We filled one with chocolate kisses that the children understood were "kisses from their mother," and they each took one daily. The other jar was filled with small paper hearts, love, and kisses ("xoxo") written on each one. The children would take a heart to hold in their hand or pocket. This was a ritual that I established earlier with Sharon, Paul, and the children to support a playful but powerful gesture of connection and love. During their final goodbye visit with Sharon, as they were leaving, Paul shared with me that Kenny would not buckle his seatbelt in the car. "There are kisses in my hand from Mommy," he told Paul, and he didn't want to lose them. Paul buckled it for him and kissed his head. "I've many kisses stored up from Mommy to give you any time."

Years later, Paul tells me that his children are doing well at school and talk about their mother frequently. He attributes the ease with which they speak *about her, and keep her alive in memories and conversations, to the care that Sharon took to ensure they openly and honestly understood her illness.*

I think about Sharon often. She was an exceptional mother whose love and dedication to her children extended long after her passing. Her story is unusual in several ways. First, Sharon reached out to support her children's understanding of her illness early in her diagnosis. I do not usually get referrals like hers, parents with young children who wish to be counselled about how to explain difficult diagnoses, treatments, and, sadly, death. Sharon was unusually prescient to have contacted me during that first visit to the oncologist. This is not to say that she was clairvoyant, nor that her doing so foreshadowed the progression of her illness and subsequent death. Rather, it was fortunate that our relationship was established early on and therefore laid a foundation for therapeutic rapport as well as her children's understanding and long-term coping.

I share this opening story because it should not be the exception. The psychosocial wellbeing of children whose lives are affected by illness is critically important to my work and mission. Sharon put into place a model for working with parents and families that should be emulated: a standard practice of care that provides for the emotional, developmental, and psychosocial wellbeing of children and families as they face the unthinkable.

Chapter 2

Context of the Work

2.1 A Hospital Setting in the Northeastern United States

I worked for almost 20 years in a Child Life and Creative Arts Therapy Department at a large children's hospital and trauma center located near New York City. Impermanence and instability permeate the hospital setting, where sickness, tragedy, and loss are ubiquitous (Omens, 2014). There is perhaps no milieu where this is more acutely felt than paediatrics.

A children's hospital houses specialized units entirely separate from adult care. Everything from a simple emergency room visit due to a playground fall, to a traumatic car accident, to chronic illness management, receives treatment specialized for children under this umbrella. Medical professionals trained to treat the individual needs of paediatric patients staff the emergency room, operating room, outpatient subspecialists, infusion rooms, inpatient, and intensive care units (ICU). Doctors, nurses, advanced specialists, respiratory therapists, clinical mental health and social service support, and many other professionals comprise the standard practice of care.

In the United States, Child Life Specialist is a national certification, and a Child Life Department must be included in the distinction of a children's hospital. Child life specialists are uniquely trained in the effects of hospitalization on the developing child. They advocate for the emotional needs of children undergoing medical procedures, focusing on education and coping. Some departments also include creative arts therapists who are experts within a specific arts modality: art, music, dance/movement, or drama. They help children develop new narratives and ways of interacting related to illness, as I will describe further in these chapters.

Within the two worlds of paediatrics and adult care, the needs of the child are not managed equally. The Child Life and Creative Arts Therapy team address the psychosocial needs of children within paediatrics. However, this objective does not extend into adult treatment areas to address the needs of children of adult patients. No direct funding is allocated specifically for a dedicated therapist who is solely focused on the therapeutic needs of these children.

On the paediatric side of the hospital, playrooms are designated as procedure-free areas where imagination and free play are protected. Consider

DOI: 10.4324/9781003026938-2

now crossing over into the adult hospital. The child is there to see their parent, perhaps for the last time. They will find no playroom and no child development specialist trained to address their developmental, emotional, and psychoeducational needs. Medical staff are focused on their adult patients, unfamiliar with how to speak with children. Some staff, themselves parents, become deeply identified with the family and frightened by the awareness that "There but for the grace of G-d go I." They might attempt to shield the child in order to distance themselves from their own mortality. Within the adult hospital, the environment is not focused on the needs of children. The child is not the patient and "family-centred care" becomes an afterthought, extending only as far as the primary partner of the patient, but with limited concern for the needs of children.

Throughout my career, I have attempted to focus on the needs of the child before me rather than the larger political issues, financial and administrative, that are ever-present in the hospital setting. Never thinking myself capable of affecting macro, systemic issues at the organizational level, I instead zoomed in on the micro: the concerns of each child, one at a time. Yet over the years, discrepancies and gaps in service between the adult and paediatric hospitals have become clear. Adult treatment approaches often lack awareness of the psychosocial needs of children affected by the complex medical issues of their parent, siblings, and loved ones.

While the wellbeing and emotional needs of sick children are essential to providing holistic care in the hospital setting, they are not the focus of this book. Paediatric care is a vast area of study and research. However, the psychosocial needs of children impacted by the illnesses of their parents, siblings, and loved ones are my passion because they are often under-addressed, overlooked, or forgotten.

2.2 The Large Urban Medical Centre in the US: Social, Economic, and Interdisciplinary Challenges

No day is the same in a hospital. Anyone who works in healthcare or has been hospitalized knows how busy, overwhelming, and chaotic a place it can be. The medical staff attend to the primary needs of the patient during long and exhausting shifts. Nurses will tell you they have little time to eat, drink, or even use the bathroom during busy times of high patient acuity. Medical staff are continually under-resourced, covering for one another in order to have short breaks. These are challenging dilemmas for every doctor, nurse, respiratory therapist, social worker, child life specialist, creative arts therapist, chaplain, and others who work in the medical centre.

From the perspective of Maslow's hierarchy (1970), we can only give when we feel we have enough left. When striving to meet our own basic needs, we can feel depleted or burnt out. This is true within any profession that demands immense output of time and energy. While periodically programs are put in place to address the personal needs of the hospital staff, often they tend to be ineffective for various reasons. Staff have patient care responsibilities and coverage is not always in place to allow them to attend. These meetings may be facilitated by a co-worker, leaving staff unsure whether confidentiality can be maintained, limiting their expression. While hospitals often offer rhetorical gestures toward the appearance of "caring for the caregiver," this is discrepant from the reality. When we experience scarcity, many of us feel a need to store up our resources, even to ration our empathy. In my years of practice, I have seen a shift in systemic hospital culture: increased corporate concern for the bottom line of profitability and an attitude encouraging staff to do more with less. In general, the message I have received regarding child life and creative arts therapy services is that they are dispensable; the weight given to understanding and providing for the psychosocial needs of children is less important than the bottom line.

The overall culture of the United States reflects similar trends: limited resources in schools, low paying jobs for teachers, and funding cuts for arts-based programming. When healthcare professionals are short of resources, this fosters an empathic lapse—a withholding of generosity—and contributes to burnout. How then can we create abundance from the inside out and back again? How can we move toward a circular system and away from a linear hierarchy, so that providers can feel cared for, thereby increasing the care we provide for others?

Emotions are not separate from our bodies; our feelings are not free-floating and distant from the self. We are our bodies and our bodies hold memories and feelings. Yet, in a highly specialized treatment model, doctors treat the body in parts. One patient may have several doctors: all specialists, all treating different parts of the body, and not necessarily orienting back to the whole. Treatment of the whole person becomes fractured. The emotional toll that diagnosis and treatment options take on the body and mind are not considered holistically, nor addressed equally.

Working with children, I help them to understand and identify two types of feeling: the way the body feels physiologically (like how the arm feels when tickled or touched) and emotional feelings (like sadness, anger, or shame). I draw this distinction for children by touching my arm softly, poking or tickling, and animating with my face, smiling or frowning, so they can more accurately understand and identify links between feelings and experiences. I do this to help them explain where the shame, anger, sadness, and feelings of all kinds manifest in their body.

The body and the mind are united. Therefore, the psychosocial and therapeutic needs of the patient should be addressed to the same level of care: a person-centred approach. This includes having therapists as integrated members of the healthcare team. At many hospitals, these needs are addressed by consultants, volunteers, or outside referrals to community-based therapists. However, having trained professionals who are accountable members of the team promotes a better healthcare culture. Rather than compartmentalizing the patient into parts, the addition of therapeutic services maintains the relationship with the whole person, promoting a higher quality of care.

In the adult section of the hospital, the words "Adult Code Blue, ICU" are announced overhead daily. They are clear and repeated three times. "Adult Code Blue, ICU." "Adult Code Blue, ICU." "Adult Code Blue, ICU." When I hear this code I think of the ICUs, and what it must be like during a code there. In the paediatric intensive care unit (PICU), a red code cart is positioned at the ready near the unstable child's room. The room is densely packed with the medical team, doctors, nurses, and respiratory therapist all surrounding the bed. This is deftly rehearsed—the choreography of the saving of a life.

Years ago, I spoke to a mother who had slept many weeks with her daughter in the PICU. She once told me that at night, hearing a code called over the intercom for another patient, she could overhear the sounds of other mothers crying. "I wonder when it will be my turn." I wonder too, when I hear the adult code, whose loved one might die. I wonder where the family is. Who, if anyone, is speaking to them, keeping them informed?

In paediatrics, I know the answers to these questions. There are psychosocial team members: the child life and creative arts therapy team, who know the child, and the social workers, who have relationships with the parents. This team works in concert to provide emotional and therapeutic support to the parents and family. They are present in meetings discussing the child and form relationships with the siblings to provide care for the whole family. These needs are considered in the children's hospital. Each child's room includes a place for a parent to sleep and areas to eat and store meals. This is not so in the main building. Waiting rooms become small campsites: the families' possessions scattered, takeout food containers in the corners of the room, and blankets stacked on chairs. Often more than one family has staked out space, delineations marking each family's small claimed territory. The adult care unit is no place for a child. It is not even conducive for the adults—no comfortable spaces to sit, no place to sleep in the room by your loved one.

Technically, the scope of my job was solely within the paediatric hospital. I was not assigned to the adult care unit; there was no funding for this. Yet, as a consultant, I found myself asked to work with children whose adult caregivers were in crisis. As I developed relationships with specific practitioners over time, these requests increased. Nurses, managers, and doctors I had worked with previously called upon my support. Progressively I expanded my practice, developing my therapeutic approach. I responded to the needs based on my understanding that all children whose lives are affected by horrific circumstances deserve therapeutic support.

2.2.1 The "Bad News Room"

When I walked onto the adult trauma unit, the nurses recognized me. "Are you here for the kids of the patient in bed eight?" one asked, and I was

brought to meet a young woman whose husband was hit by a car while out for a weekend bike ride. She started to speak with me about her three children and what to tell them, how to explain this. This was perhaps one of the most serious conversations she would ever have, telling the most important people in her life that their father would never come home again. That he would never again celebrate Christmas, wake them from bed on a cold Monday morning for school—so many things, that telling them was unimaginable. In our conversation, I addressed what to tell the children and how to explain death to them. I discussed having the children visit to say goodbye to their daddy. This pivotal conversation took place in a small converted closet, a space designated for the nurses to change into their scrubs, with an adjacent bathroom and metal lockers lining the walls. I brought tissues, but knew they would be small and rough. This was the best I could do in order to find a private space to speak with her.

The body holds memories of all human experiences (van der Kolk, 2014). We can remember where we were and whom we were with when we hear certain music, smell the scent of a flower, or watch the light change during nightfall. Some of the most meaningful moments in a person's life take place in the hospital. Within its rooms, babies are born, and lives are forever changed by illness or ended by death. Yet little attention is paid to the environment. A primary example is the room used to deliver "bad news," which exists in every unit of the hospital. Among staff, it might be known as the "Bad News Room." Patients, doctors, and medical staff know that when a family is led to this place, bad news will be delivered. This room is forever imprinted in the families' minds; therefore, attention needs to be paid to the objects, sounds, and smells. These rooms should be filled with healing and supportive images, smells, sounds, and textures to promote the most therapeutically beneficial experience. Instead, they are often littered with papers from previous meetings, projector screens, and harsh fluorescent lights. Yet the rest of the hospital is a place of highly specialized environments: operating rooms, ambulances, medical transport helicopters—all carefully designed for their purposes. Creating designated places to have difficult conversations helps promote and support emotional wellbeing for families and patients.

Sometimes due to time demands on the staff, bad news is shared in a more liminal space, even the most public of places, like hallways or shared patient rooms. Given the significance of the information being shared, even during a crisis, "bad news" should be delivered in a specialized manner, with care that reflects the weight of the events. Just as treatment of the knee is a particular specialization, different from treatment of the hip joint, caring for the emotional needs of the patient and family hearing difficult information is also a specialized skill. Addressing life-altering information is within the specialty of the therapist. Can we improve upon the delivery with which we share information, including the locations we deliver it in? Shouldn't bad news also be shared by the staff members who are better equipped to deliver it? From this dramatherapist's perspective, we can set the stage, rehearse our lines, and direct the scene in order to perform a more supportive and therapeutic experience.

Psychological understanding of post-traumatic stress indicates that trauma encodes memories filled with smells, visual imagery, sound, and texture (Levine, 1997; van der Kolk, 2014). These memories of the traumatic event are triggered in part by sensorial experiences, and then "flashes" of memories are once again reexperienced and remembered in the body. As healthcare providers within institutions promoting optimal care, we can mitigate the trauma of difficult events, making these encoded experiences healthier. When we know that a birth is pending, or an illness is not compatible with life, medical professionals can address the mind as much as the body, creating a protected place to provide the medical interventions needed and promote optimal care.

Chapter 3

Dramatherapy and Child Life

In order to explore the application of this work, we must first establish a foundational understanding of dramatherapy, child life, and grief work with children. In this chapter, I will review key terms and definitions, followed by an illustrative case study. Finally, I will synthesize core shared principles between dramatherapy and child life that inform my approach.

3.1 Dramatherapy: Key Definitions and Terms

Dramatherapy is a form of psychotherapy that implements clinical interventions rooted in theatre arts. Dramatherapists are masters-level mental health professionals who practice in a variety of settings, including psychiatric hospitals, outpatient clinics, medical hospitals, criminal justice settings, and private practice with individuals across the lifespan.

Dramatherapists utilize embodied, active techniques to facilitate therapeutic change, including role play, storytelling, improvisation, projection, and performance (North American Drama Therapy Association, 2017). The specific modality of treatment is chosen depending on the clinical goal, the needs of the client, and the practitioner's theoretical orientation. Clients can find new flexibility and perform the changes and interactions within the therapy that they wish to realize in their lives.

3.1.1 The Application of Dramatherapy with Children and Adolescents

Dramatherapy provides a developmentally appropriate means of processing events with children and adolescents, when verbal methods alone may be limiting. Benefits include reducing feelings of isolation, developing new coping skills, and adjusting patterns of behaviour by broadening an individual's range for the expression of feelings. An increased sense of play can improve self-esteem, self-worth, spontaneity, and relationship development. In addition, play and spontaneity allow children to gain mastery over internal conflicts and anxiety. Play taps into a child's natural tendencies towards action and engages them to safely

DOI: 10.4324/9781003026938-3

explore issues, painful feelings, and experiences. Often children do not communicate their feelings and thoughts directly. However, the dramatherapist is clinically trained to offer support through the language of play—including toys, objects, and stories.

The following techniques represent a selection of interventions that are relevant to the work included within this book.

Role Play is a primary process during child development. Children in play are constantly moving in and out of role, not only to entertain themselves, but also to deepen their understanding of the world by taking on, playing out, and changing characters. Robert Landy's role theory and role method (2007) explore role as an effective way for clients to recognize behaviours and make meaningful changes. In role theory, clients identify, play out, and explore their own roles as well as the roles of others they encounter in their lives. Stepping in and out of role can also facilitate changes in perspective.

Metaphor is commonly used in everyday life as a way of holding meaning. This use of comparison is a way of transferring meaning from one thing to another and can improve understanding, make moments memorable, and support positive change. The use of metaphor can help clients see situations from an alternative perspective or a more comfortably distanced viewpoint. This perspective shift, what Landy (2007) termed *aesthetic distance*, can make distressing experiences more palatable, foster objectivity, and enhance decision making.

Projective Object Play uses toys, puppets, masks, and objects in order to allow clients to express their feelings through external images. Projective play also provides an opportunity for the dramatherapist to make a clinical assessment and explore issues in an interactive manner with clients. The process of creating a projective, object such as a puppet or mask, can itself be part of the therapeutic intervention. Clients imbue their creations with specific qualities and abilities, enhancing the safety of expression by increasing aesthetic distance. Interventions might also include role play or enactment using created objects.

Psychodrama/Sociodrama are action methods in which clients use spontaneous dramatization, role playing, and dramatic self-exploration to gain insight into their lives (Garcia & Buchanan, 2009). Psychodrama includes interventions such as doubling, mirroring, role reversal, the empty chair technique, and other dramatic structures of theatre as a form of psychotherapy.

Improvisation invites creative, dramatic interaction without script or preparation, encouraging spontaneity. Improvisation techniques create greater possibilities for increased imagination. These experiential encounters privilege free play and spontaneous flow. Theatre artist Viola Spolin (1999) developed many exercises designed to unleash creativity and unlock individuals' abilities to create and express themselves. Johnson's (2009) developmental transformations method builds on her techniques.

Developmental Transformations is a form of dramatherapy developed by David Read Johnson that uses free association in action through movement.

It establishes a dramatic *playspace*, the therapeutic arena, into which the client and therapist enter. Clients mutually agree to participate in play that is both real—tapping into the client's real stories, issues, or conditions—and make believe, occurring in a *surplus reality*. The therapeutic contract is to engage in this modality in order to help the client feel less constrained by fears of unpredictability, changes, and traumatic experiences of life (Johnson 2009, 2013; Omens, 2014).

When a story is difficult to tell or contains painful or traumatic events, it can be hard to talk about or remember. *Therapeutic* use of story allows aesthetic distancing of those events: a concrete telling that includes a beginning, middle, and end that can be revisited (Emunah, 1994). This process allows children or adults to gain confidence in telling their story in the way that they want. For children, it can also increase emotional literacy and the ability to regulate emotion as it relates to those events. Storytelling provides clients with opportunities to "rescript" their experience.

3.2 Child Life with Children Who Are Grieving

The child life profession began in North America in the 1920s with the mission to improve children's experiences in the healthcare system (Association of Child Life Professionals, n.d.). Child life specialists work to reduce the negative short- and long-term effects of inpatient and outpatient care. Through the use of non-directive play, child life specialists provide explanations and preparations for procedures. They use the principles of child development to support a child's ability to cope with the demands of the hospital experience, whether treatment is for the child or their sibling (Romito *et al.*, 2020).

By assessing their coping strategies, the child life specialist promotes the child's optimal development when facing medical challenges. Helping children to understand the medical situation and clarifying confusing concepts provides them with greater knowledge, which improves overall coping. Without explanation, children can have misconceptions and confusion about medical equipment, which create more anxiety, fearfulness, and distrust of medical staff. Play is the preferred language of the child: it is through play that children process and learn. Play is deep work. It is also through play that we can understand children's fears and thought processes.

Whether by avoiding what we see during times of stress or by moving closer in towards the situation, we all cope somewhere on this spectrum. Imagine, for example, a routine blood test. Some of us prefer to watch what is happening rather than look away. We might wish to engage, integrating the observable visuals—the tourniquet, the needle, the blood sample—with the physical experience we are having. Others prefer to look away, finding a spot on the wall to focus on, talking or thinking about something else, distracting themselves from the physical sensations with alternative stimulation. Some people are a mix of the two, falling somewhere in between, perhaps even interchanging both coping styles during the time from start to finish of the procedure. This "avoidance versus sensitizing" coping process (Peterson, 1989) is true for everyone, and it is observable during painful experiences like invasive medical procedures. I have also observed this in children during times of stress when there is disbelief: a dissociation between what has been previously understood about the body and what is currently being seen. This split can happen when what we are seeing is unusual, previously unimagined, and disparate from normality.

Most of us are familiar with children "playing doctor" and pretending other routine life events in order to understand their experiences. The movie Toy Story (1995) is a miraculous world where beloved children's toys interact and come to life, a world where the quality and importance of a toy are truly elevated. Its sequel, Toy Story 2 (1999), offers a glimpse into a child's processing of surgical experience. In one scene, Sid, Sally's bratty older brother sees his sister playing with her doll. He informs his sister that her doll is "sick" and he must perform an operation. He plays through the whole scene, preparing the operating room for surgery and calling to an imaginary nurse for assistance. He goes to work on the doll with pliers, and emerges to proudly announce to his sister that she's "fixed": he has replaced the doll's head with the head of a pterodactyl. Up in his room, Sid considered this operation to be a successful "triple bypass and brain transplant." Though in the story of the movie this scene demonstrates Sid's cruelty, its representation of real play allows the film to also explore deep fears of powerlessness and confusion experienced by many children when confronting medical situations.

Fears like these are very real for a child when they enter the hospital, whether for a simple examination, a minor procedure, or hospitalization. These fears also emerge when a child comes to visit a loved one. The hospital environment, doctors, and nurses can be scary for children. This can be in large part because, like Sid, they magnify or distort procedures that doctors perform. From my clinical perspective, a child who plays like Sid would make me curious about his previous medical experiences. From Sid's abrupt snatching of his sister's doll, I might infer a child not being properly prepared for examinations, pulled away from his parents and quickly whisked away to a procedure room, without preparation or explanation. I could also imagine Sid having past, non-medical experiences, of not being in control that could be enacted through the metaphor of the surgical procedure. Playing the role of the surgeon means that, this time, he is in control.

It is common for parents, doctors, or nurses to lie to children. "This will not hurt," they say, without validating the child's fears and concerns about pain. Many children have had medical staff sneak up on them and surprise them with a procedure. As the nurse prepares to give a vaccination, she might say, "Okay, 1, 2, 3." However, she gives the shot on count two, not three as predicted by the child, therefore violating the child's feelings of safety. These seemingly mild breaches of trust create distress in the child, as interpreted by Sid's sadistic snatching of his sister's doll and cruel treatment towards her.

When a child is affected by a parent's or sibling's potentially life-limiting diagnosis, many parents and healthcare providers are at a loss to help them understand the situation and work through their feelings. In hospitals, child life specialists are integrated members of the multidisciplinary care team, advocating for the child's integral role in the family system. Siblings are not to be left out when end-of-life situations affect patient care. Holistic patient- and family-centered care includes an understanding that all members of the family are grieving and that the unique needs of the children require specialized professionals. This is the role of the child life specialist.

For grieving children of parents dying while on adult care units, most hospitals do not have child life support. Yet special attention is required in order for children not to become a forgotten piece of their family's puzzle in the moment of the loss. Often families will ask me if the death of a parent or sibling will be traumatic for children. Yes, of course, these are tragic events and traumatic. But including the child through therapeutic interventions helps them grieve through and process in real time, during the moment of trauma. The healing is concurrent with the event, rather than afterward. In lieu of waiting to intervene post-trauma, where most therapeutic interventions are conducted, in this work I address the nature of events as they are occurring. The sessions do not necessarily prevent the need for future therapy, but interventions can offer the child opportunities to actively participate, a clear understanding of the process occurring, and ways to express themselves (Omens, 2014). We cannot prevent death; however, we can support children to work through the trauma.

3.2.1 A Date to Remember: A Story Told in Two Acts (Act I)
ॐ

On the day of her 37th birthday, a young mother of two was pronounced brain dead. Having suffered a life-ending car accident, she was brought to the ICU where her devastated husband sat holding her hand, praying by her side. He wanted to know how to talk to his children. Along with members of his wife's medical team, I sat with him in a small conference room. That room will forever be the "bad news room" remembered by this young father. On the table was half a box of tissues—perhaps left behind by the last family to cry in this room. We sat down and he told me that his daughters, Olivia (8 years old) and her sister Lily (10 years old), had been asking him when their mommy would be home and if they could visit with her. He, too heartbroken to tell them the truth, had said she was getting better and would be home soon. Later the girls would ask me about this: why everyone in their family had lied to them for days, telling them she was getting better and not to worry.

Their father hoped to delay any explanations and, therefore, not need to bring the children to see their mother. He feared how upset they would be seeing her. "Yes, it's very upsetting," I told him, adding that one would expect them to be upset. We explored how he envisioned this playing out. He wondered if it was better for him to "warm them up" to the idea (in his words, "soften the blow"). He told me the way he imagined shielding them from the reality that his wife was brain dead and that, later that night, she would be removed from the ventilator. He planned that he could tell the girls their mother needed surgery "for a broken leg" and unfortunately "died during the operation." "That wouldn't be the truth," I told him. I explained that he could only control what he told the children, when and how, but not what others would say, or what they might see on social media or be told at school. Many people in their town, as well as the extended family, knew what had happened, and it would not be possible to hold others to the version of the story he imagined. He communicated to me that he could not find the strength to explain all of this to his daughters. He asked me to speak to them directly.

I told him that he should go home and prepare them for their visit by explaining that he had spoken to a lady, Stephanie, whose job was to talk to children when their mothers were in the hospital, and that she would take them to see their mother. Their father understood that Olivia and Lily needed to come to the hospital to have an opportunity to be with their mother and say goodbye. Allowing them to see her and telling them the truth were things he could control. But what he truly wished to control were the events that took his wife's life—that earlier that week, without warning, on an otherwise peaceful, bright sunny day, suddenly a devastating accident occurred that he could not have stopped. There was no controlling this—not for her, for him, or for the girls.

In preparation for the children to visit, I had to set the stage, having rehearsed similar scenes many times before. In this story, that setting was a young mother's hospital room on her 37th birthday. I looked at the room: the patient, the respirator, the IV poles, and all the other medical equipment. I went about making the room as child friendly as possible within the limitations of the ICU. I arranged a recent photo of the children and their mother smiling in a prominent spot on the bedside table. A soft blanket with cozy kittens replaced the plain white hospital linen. A bright pretty scarf for their mother's head covered the bandages. Relatives brought balloons that dangled in the corners of the room and a few other birthday decorations, all of which created a more personalized atmosphere. I added some plush teddy bears and toys for the children, available to use for projective play (see Chapter 3.1).

I met the family in the unit lobby. The girls walked towards me, looking hesitant and afraid. Olivia and Lily had not seen their mother in days and were unclear as to why. While these two frightened young children had witnessed the frequent phone calls, hushed voices, and arrivals of distant relatives, what they saw and heard did not coincide with the story they were being told. They came to the hospital with their father and grandmother. The younger child wore a fuzzy soft sweater with a shiny unicorn on the front and sneakers that glittered. Her older sister had her hair neatly brushed and pulled back in a ponytail—just the way I imagine her mother would have done it. However, her grandmother may have had to do her hair today, as her mother could not. The girls carried colored birthday cards for her.

I explained that I was a dramatherapist who meets with children when their parent is in the hospital. "The hospital is a big place and the kids I work with often have questions about why their parent is here and what it will be like to see them," I told them. I said that I use play to find ways to tell the story to answer some of these questions. "It's not easy to have Mommy in the hospital and I will try to make it a little easier, even though I know it is not easy at all." Then we all went upstairs to my office. The anxiety I had sensed from the children in the lobby seemed to have faded, as they sat before me and looked curiously at the markers and two plain muslin cloth dolls I had prepared for this session. I also had crayons, coloured paper, and a few children's books about anatomy and the body. My role was to explore the girls' current understanding of what had happened and any misconceptions they had, as well as to answer their questions and provide psychoeducational and emotional support.

"Do you know which part of Mommy's body is hurt?" This is often where I begin. When explaining a medical condition to children, I differentiate the parts of the body, defining and exploring what parts of the body do in relationship to the whole self. I clarify for the child about disorders of the body and what is known about the prognosis. As their father had previously asked me to do, I also explained the extent of their mothers' injuries and her diagnosis: that she was brain dead.

The dolls were stuffed medical play dolls, without any features of the face or body. I sat back to see what drew the children's interest. They each picked up a doll, examining them. "These dolls are missing something. Would you like to give your dolls a face?" They began drawing eyes, noses, and mouths on their dolls. As they did, I defined: "Their eyes are great, now they can see. What things can they see with their eyes?" I asked the same about the other parts of the face, defining the functions of each. I was setting the stage for a deeper understanding of other parts of the body, and the jobs they do in order to make the body work.

I drew on construction paper and used picture books to show them other parts of the body. I asked them if I could draw on the other side of their dolls. Invoking a component of Role Theory (Landy, 2007), I used the doll to reveal a more in-depth representation of the body parts inside, allowing me to further explain how the sad realities of their mother's injuries affected different systems of her body. The girls were engaged and participated, helping me draw and talking about what they knew. "The heart is for pumping the blood throughout the whole body and the lungs provide oxygen," I explained. I spoke too about the digestive system, nervous system, and the brain, the many *different roles in the body system and the parts they play. "These are all important parts of the body, working together to keep the body healthy and strong, but when one part is hurt, the other parts are affected." This is the scaffolding I construct, supporting even a very young child to understand death and dying. Children as young as 1 or 2 years old understand the concepts of working and broken. They know when a beloved toy is beyond repair and also when it can be fixed.*

The use of play, the preferred language of children, and the dramatic realm invite children to enter worlds that masquerade as real. As we get lost in the drama, we are transported from everyday reality, into what can only be imagined. Imagination is limitless and here we can play with nonrealities and death—the previously unimaginable and unplayable. Dramatherapy is a form of communication not limited by a child's age, the language they speak, their culture, or cognitive ability. It is a potentially more pleasant and non-threatening means of self-expression within the therapeutic relationship that facilitates physical, psychological, cognitive, and emotional development. Symbolism and metaphor are used to promote expression and meaning. During end-of-life work, I use play and hope to instill possibilities for what is unimaginable around us.

When I asked the girls to share their understanding, they knew that their mother was in an accident. When I asked how they believed she was hurt, they told me she had broken her leg. That is consistent with what many children like these girls have told me. Children often locate some type of concrete injury they can imagine: something they can conceive of happening if a person falls and is seriously injured. A broken leg was far from the injuries their mother suffered on that sunny day. When a car turned the corner without seeing her just as she had stepped into the street, their mother was struck by the car, fell hard, instantly suffering a life-limiting brain bleed—a brain injury that the first responders, emergency room trauma team, and neurosurgeons were unable to repair.

In all cases of explaining complicated medical situations to children, I start from what the child knows and understands about the body and then expand upon this using developmentally appropriate vocabulary, drawings, and pictures to help them understand what has happened and how this affects the whole body. For these eight- and ten-year-old girls, I used books like *Understanding the Human Body: Anatomy Made Easy for Kids* (Tucker, 2021) and *Knowledge Encyclopaedia Human Body!* (DK & Smithsonian Institute, 2017). These provide concrete examples of the body's vascular and nervous systems. I explained how their mother fell, about the very bad injury to her head and the bleeding under her skull in her brain. "If her brain isn't working—the part that understands words, and meaning—then she won't be able to hear us when we say that we're here with her, when we say that we love her," said the ten-year-old, making both a statement and asking me a hopeful question, tears rolling down her cheeks. "What do you think?" I asked. She told me she was not sure. I said that I was not either. She was right, the parts of her mother's brain that process language, the temporal lobe and auditory cortex, were no longer working. Brain death and blood flow study confirmed that. After bleeding that could not be stopped by surgery, her injuries were irreparable and conclusive. I could see that she was thinking, trying to solve this unsolvable problem. "What about … " she struggled to find the words, "A brain transplant?" A great idea! She was smart and thoughtful, imagining ways to fix it, to reverse what she was coming to understand was true. She was playing with ideas, using her imagination to process and come to acceptance. It is not easy to accept the unacceptable.

The girls explored with me many ways this could be fixed and I went through this with them, until we came to the inevitable question: how could she get better if her brain was so badly hurt? The answer I provided: she could not get better, and her body not recovering meant that she would not survive. "But how will she get better?" they asked. I looked to their father, asking him if he could answer their question. He shook his head, indicating to me that I should answer. I gently told them that their mother would die from this. Then I paused, and said nothing, allowing them to process the words. Often I have witnessed families rushing to break the stillness at this moment, as if there is anything further to say that will fill the silence following the word just spoken: "die."

The girls were seated close to their father and grandmother, who cradled them in their arms where they could be comforted as they cried. Their grief was heartbreaking. I told them how I wished this was not true, that I wished there was something else that the doctors and nurses could do.

Children of all ages are smart and will explore ways in which the problem can be solved, trying to find logical ways to fix the situation. After a long time crying, Olivia and Lily asked me questions. There were no words that could solve this, only love and the comfort of their father's lap. There was no solution to the finality of death.

What else could we imagine? What could be hoped for, and what could we believe to be true? "I've never been able to ask someone who's brain dead what they hear or don't hear," I tell her. "There is a part of us that knows love, that part, and I'm not sure where it is. We can't draw that part on the doll." We talked about that, about love and where the children felt their mother's love and where their love might be located within their mother. Everyone in the room, their father, grandmother, and I, could feel that love. I asked them about their mother, to tell me stories so that I could know her too. Even though we had never met before that day, I knew about her through the stories and looks in her daughters' eyes. Their father told the story of how they met. They met at the store where she worked and he told me that she wanted to go out with him, so she took his number from his order information and called him every day until he would ask her out. The girls began to giggle and then broke into laughter. "That's not true, Daddy. You were the one who begged her to go out with you, and went to the shop every day asking her, until she finally said, 'yes.'"

In their laughter and this story, I can feel something "other." The girls told me several stories about their mom, and I encouraged them to share more. I got glimpses into this family's life, seeing and feeling the humour, joy, and love they shared. Later when we were in the ICU, in her room, these are the moments we talked about with their mother, recollecting together, as we honoured her life, even though she left that life behind.

My assessment while working with these children and others like them is based on the needs and the time it takes to meet the established goals. Typically, intake assessments and subsequent sessions last somewhere between 45 and 60 minutes. If a situation seems to require more than that, I must be clear about what the clinical needs are that dictate a longer session time. I have learned to maintain these boundaries, considering the emotional toll it takes on both the children and me. This dilemma is heightened because no funding is allocated to create a program (see Chapter 2), meaning that resources are limited to address the extremely important needs of these children.

At the time of a paediatric death in the children's hospital, there are legacy items to offer the parents: meaningful objects that are cherished forever. When working with a child grieving the death of their parent, I offer legacy-making for the children to create. Legacy items are ways to memorialize and honor a loved one's memories. A variety of expressive arts therapy interventions can enhance expression and coping with a death. Some examples include making moulds of their loved one's hand, taking thumbprints, assembling photo books, or creating films or music that support grieving. These provide the child with concrete objects that capture the personhood and humanity of their parent for them to hold onto and bring home, even though their parent cannot come home with them.

In this case, while I was with Olivia and Lily at their mother's bedside, I picked up and placed their mother's hand onto a plain white pillowcase. Then I asked the girls to choose a coloured marker. I carefully traced the outline of their mother's hand, making an imprint of her hand on the pillowcase. We made one pillowcase for each girl, for them to take home, place in their beds, and sleep with the imprint of their mother's loving hands holding them. I explained that we could draw their mother's handprint onto a canvas and paint it for them to take home too.

There is no algorithm or checklist prescribing the legacy items to make with a grieving child. I provide similar interventions to many families, but they are customized for each child, incorporating their family's stories and their special relationship with their loved one, parent, or sibling. During these tragedies, I wish I had some magic spell to make it all better, but sadly I do not. Instead, I translate the tragic events into the language of children. I provide them with a concrete symbol of their relationship to come home with them when their loved one cannot.

3.3 Dramatherapy with Children Who Are Grieving

All the world's a stage,
And all the men and women merely players;
They have their exits and their entrances,

And one man in his time plays many parts, [...]
Last scene of all,
That ends this strange eventful history,
Is second childishness and mere oblivion,
Sans teeth, sans eye, sans taste, sans everything.
(Shakespeare, *As You Like It,* 1623/2011, 2.7.139–166)

If all the world's a stage, then death is the final act. Over the course of life, we slowly approach the final curtain call. Some deaths are more abrupt: an ending too soon, before all the acts of life are complete. The deaths of infants, children, or young parents are sudden and shocking—lives cut short. These are like leaving the theatre at intermission, unable to return to watch the drama complete its natural ending.

I have listened to parents, doctors, and nurses who do not want to talk to children about death. I have explored their resistance and concerns: the information will be sad and the children will cry; they are too young to understand; or they are too little to even remember this loss. Some parents express that they feel the situation is too complex and will be confusing for their child to understand. These are intelligent, caring people with fears and defences against confronting this sad, yet inevitable and natural part of life.

I am often consulted at the eleventh hour when there is no more medicine to offer and no possibility that the dying patient will be able to come home again. I am called in to help when those families who believe in prayer are praying for miracles, and nonbelievers seek hope when it seems hopeless. Dramatherapy can offer hope to children during times of anticipatory grief and bereavement: in the face of what is, the imagination of what could be.

Each family's needs and stories are different. Over time, however, common themes have emerged to inform and guide my practice. The hard, stark reality of death is one we would all wish to shield a child from. Yet fairy tales often begin with the death of a parent (Bettelheim, 1976). The telling and retelling of these fables support a child's understanding of inevitable life experiences. Just as there is often a "happy ending," the child can retain the understanding that they, too, will survive. Fairy tales teach us, "that a struggle against severe difficulties in life is unavoidable, is an intrinsic part of human existence—but if one does not shy away, but steadfastly meets unexpected and often unjust hardships, one masters all obstacles and at the end emerges victorious" (p. 8).

The powerful foundations of drama—dramatic metaphor, principles of stage direction, and storytelling—are natural vehicles for this work. When I walk onto the scene, there is a lack of direction. The production is in a moment of chaos. Through my interventions, I reconfigure the stage. I collaborate with the auxiliary players: the patient (the lead actor), family members, and medical team. The cacophonous sounds of the medial equipment and unit activity become our orchestration. I set the stage for the dramatic action of the next act.

In some cases, this involves clearing the room of relatives and friends, allowing children to have a private visit with only the key essential players.

3.3.1 A Date to Remember: A Story Told in Two Acts (Act II)

ॐ

I led 8-year-old Lily and 10-year-old Olivia down the hall to their mother's room. While walking, I stood close to convey a secure and confident presence; I was not afraid to go where we were going. I told them: "This is the hallway to the unit, and around the corner will be your mother's room. The curtain to her room is closed and first you will meet her nurses." I watch the children closely in order to intuit nonverbal responses about their coping. From this position I can provide guidance to them as I sense how they are managing the stress of the environment, and offer the direction needed, choreographing their entrance. I anticipate the various movements: either a slow entrance onto the stage, moving in close; or standing back hesitantly.

I directed them to stand near the doorway and to take a moment before they entered the room. The "moment before" is a term from the theatre, referring to how the actor prepares for their entrance onto the stage. This technique allows the actor to take a moment to consider the emotions, thoughts and feelings their character experiences just moments before the action is to begin. I too, take a moment's pause, to be in touch with my feelings and what I imagine the girls are feeling. In this moment before the entrance, we pause as the curtain opens, they stand in the doorway and can see their mother from the doorway. They could then decide if they wanted to go into the room or not. I watched their reactions, their breathing, their body movements. I observed so that I could adjust for their needs at this moment: their entrance onto this stage. I had arranged one chair near the bed, so that they could sit or kneel on to be closer to her, and one chair further away, should they want to stay nearer to the door.

The director of a play must maintain an overall vision for the production, both by collaborating with the actors and by providing a supportive space for expression. She might take an actor aside to help them bridge the gap between the next two emotional moments in the action. As therapist and director, I follow the child's affect. For example, if I see an indication that tears are being held back, I may offer an invitation to cry as permission to the child to express their feelings. Just as a film director zooms in on a character during an important moment, I zoom in on the child, putting other elements of the hospital scene into the background to centre their experience. This reframes the typical hospital narrative which relegates the child to the background of the scene. Unlike a typical day in the ICU, normal operations of the hospital are suspended to integrate the child. This gives greater meaning, putting "patient- and family-centred care" in action.

On the stage, the precise positions of each actor are known as *blocking*. The blocking informs the actors where to stand during each line when to cross the stage, sit, stand, or turn with precision during the play. As the children entered, I provided options for their "blocking" in order to support their needs by positioning them in the room. I narrated what they saw, integrating the visuals with their cognitive understanding while supporting their emotional responses. This required sensitivity as these elements were unique for each daughter.

There was a slow intake of the truths in the room as the children integrated the images we talked about beforehand. Drawing pictures and talking about what they would see is different from the actual body in the hospital bed. The parent before them contrasted with the images and other memories mixed in from the last time they saw their mother, perhaps standing in the kitchen or waking them for school. The scene takes time to emerge, like improvisation happening in the moment. There is no script, each child reacting differently along a spectrum of wanting to be nearer to or further away from their parent. In this case, I had prepared the space and the girls to the greatest extent possible in order to accommodate their responses.

Slowly we entered and 8-year-old Olivia readily went to her mother. This was consistent with her developmental understanding and integration of the information she knew and the physical presence of her mother's body. I encouraged her as she reached out for her mother's hand. I asked if she wanted to kiss her. Her father helped his daughter kiss his wife's hand.

10-year-old Lily was more reluctant, hesitating to approach. Her emotional reaction was consistent with her age. Lily initially appeared to struggle to fully integrate what she saw, needing more time to process. She looked shocked both emotionally and physically, processing differently from her younger sister. I turned back to her and suggested she sit in the chair nearest the door. She sat silently and I took deep breaths with her, slow and steady, reassuring her it was okay just to sit nearby and not go in if she didn't want to now. After a few moments, I asked if she wanted to leave the room and she did. Her aunt and I brought her out of the room, while their father stayed inside with his youngest daughter by his wife's bedside. As she sat outside her mother's room, we continued practicing slow, deep breaths. She told me she felt strange in her mother's room and could feel her own heart pounding, as if she wanted to cry, yet could not. "That's okay," I told her, "This is really hard and it's not normal to see your mom like this." I reassured her and she remained outside the room with her aunt while I went back in to see her sister.

The youngest was kneeling on the chair, boosted up so that she could lean over and reach her mother, kissing and touching her. Sensing her desire to be near her mother, I asked her if she wanted to lie down with her. The nurse made room for the child and we placed some pillows behind her and helped her lay at her mother's side. We positioned her mother's arm around her, so she could feel her mother's touch. The child cuddled her mother, her head on her chest, and her little arm across her mother's belly. "I can hear her heart beating," she said. This moment, the feel of her mother's warmth, her hand around her, and the sound of her beating heart, as her head rested on mommy's chest, all required choreography. We were staging this moment so that she could feel her mother for the last time.

What do we say in a time like this? It is often hard to find the words or even speak at all during such a visit. The conversation is difficult and I have found that children need help verbalizing. Again, we can look at the theatre as a guide. Like the classical Greek Chorus or the contemporary role of the "stage manager" in Thornton Wilder's *Our Town* (1938/2020), I take on the role of the narrator. I can provide voice to the character for the audience and offer ways to move the action forward. Narration is a technique whereby one or more performers speak directly to the audience to tell a story, give information, or comment on the action of the scene or the motivations of characters.

When words are hard to find, I offer children lines like a prompter. Using the psychodramatic technique of *doubling* (Garcia & Buchanan, 2009), I give voice to the words I believe the child might wish to say. As the youngest child approached the bed, the silence in the room became very loud. "You can tell mommy you're here," I said. This offers the child a voice and allows underlying feelings the opportunity to emerge. I spoke for Olivia, adopting a similar posture while making eye contact with her and saying in her voice, "Mommy, I'm here and I love you very much." The child nodded and repeated this to her mother. "I love you, Mommy," she said. Adopting the role of the narrator again, I continue: "Your mother cannot tell you she's happy you're here and she loves you too," I said, "but if she could she would say how very much she loves you and loves having you with her." I will also say the words I imagine their parent speaking, or look to the patient's spouse to ask what they would answer. These conversations are often the last opportunity for children to give voice to feelings while in the presence of their parent's body. I make room for silence, too, when there truly are no words—when the love and sorrow in the room need no sound.

3.4 The Intersection of Dual Roles: Dramatherapist and Child Life Specialist

The whole is greater than the sum of its parts. The whole can be split, but any one of the parts alone is less than the whole. This philosophy is fundamental to body function, team dynamics, mathematics, Gestalt psychology, and family systems. The body is a container of parts: organs, nerves, muscles, etc. Each individually plays a role, yet also functions as part of an ensemble, performing the whole play. As a "hybrid" myself—a clinician who applies more than one theory, playing more than one part—I know there is strength in integration.

However, in my experience, institutions tend to separate these modalities, delineating the differences rather than connections. Creative arts therapists working in paediatric hospitals, whether within or separate from child life departments, implement their modalities in service of the whole child's coping and wellbeing. In some cases, creative arts therapy is a separate department. In others, it is ancillary or includes artists-in-residence and paraprofessionals but not therapists. These distinctions are primarily the concern of administration and human resources, i.e., departmental growth and funding streams. Dissecting differences between creative arts modalities (art, music, dance/movement, dramatherapy) or between the mental health professions (social work, counselling) can create power conflicts and shame dynamics (Johnson, 1994). The marrying of different modalities in clinical practice, when approached in an integrated way, can strengthen patient-centred care.

My theoretical approach throughout this book is based upon my clinical practice at the intersection of dramatherapy and child life. In my work, these two disciplines are integrally sewn together. This book is not intended to outline the differences between the two, but rather to highlight how both have informed my work in bereavement with children and families. As a supervisor and teacher, my understanding of being a dramatherapist within a child life creative arts therapy department has deepened my work.

Both dramatherapy and child life centralize the healing power of play. They also both involve the use of materials to create playful interactions with children, as a means of self-expression and to better understand the world. The child life profession understands that play is an essential developmental process and the importance of promoting to the greatest degree possible normative play, as a child would otherwise be engaged in at home and school, during the hospital experience. Therapeutic play contributes to a child's emotional wellbeing while inside the hospital walls: "Play constitutes an essential parameter of the normal psycho-somatic development of children as well as their statutory right. It is also an important means of communication in childhood" (Koukourikos *et al.*, 2015, p. 440).

Dramatherapy is a graduate level professional and licensed in New York State. Child life specialists can obtain certification at both undergraduate and graduate levels. The American Academy of Paediatrics and the National Association of Children's Hospitals and Related Institutions recognize the importance of child life departments as the benchmark standard in Pediatric Centers (Romito *et al.*, 2020).

Both modalities have competencies which include knowledge of theories of child development and the grieving child. Each specialty applies these theories to support children affected by hospital circumstances. Child life specialists facilitate memory-making experiences, providing grieving families with lasting memories when a child dies. These tokens will never replace the devastating losses, but many families treasure a lock of hair tied in a bow and placed into a shadow box. Other keepsakes include painting the child's hand or foot onto a canvas board, which the family can frame, or recording their heartbeat. When facilitating memory-making with children and families I incorporate story, role play, metaphor, and imagination, as they are foundational to dramatherapy.

I apply principles of storytelling, Landy's (2007) Role Theory, and Johnson's (2009, 2013) Developmental Transformations (DvT) in my work. From a child life perspective, I incorporate medical play using real and unreal medical objects with children, in order to explore their understanding and help them express concerns about their medical experience.

Chapter 4

Intersections of Hospital, Drama, and Death

4.1 Intersections of Life and Theatre

> Therefore the moon, the governess of floods,
> Pale in her anger, washes all the air,
> That rheumatic diseases do abound:
> And thorough this distemperature we see
> The seasons alter: [...] the spring, the summer,
> The childing autumn, angry winter, change
> Their wonted liveries, and the mazed world,
> By their increase, now knows not which is which:
> And this same progeny of evils comes
> From our debate, from our dissension;
> We are their parents and original.
> (Shakespeare, *A Midsummer Night's Dream,* 1600/2011, 2.1.103-117)

Dramatherapy, which involves play, can seem at odds with the severity and seriousness of death. Outwardly it may appear that children should not be made privy to this process and that mixing dramatherapy with bereaved children could be potentially harmful, like jumping into deep water without knowing how to swim. A balance, however, can be found.

I have always found balance near the ocean. Watching the movement of the tide, I meditate on the moon's power. I love the repetitive convergence of water and sand, as each wave moves up on the shore and is met by the pulling back of the one before. The ebb and flow reveal the tension as the gravitational pull of the Earth and the moon control high and low tides on opposing sides of the planet. The tidal change is unfailingly faithful. I find this calming, dramatic, and therapeutic.

The changes made along the shoreline are an improvisational and creative process, each tiny grain of sand moving, creating imperceptible outcomes. Can the constancy of the movement be soothing, knowing at the same time that evolution is beyond our control? Therapeutic change can be this way: small, slow transformation with change becoming clearer over time. Dramatherapy

DOI: 10.4324/9781003026938-4

plays with the telling and retelling of our stories, increasing our tolerance for the changes in our lives.

The ocean is a playground for me, and I play with my tolerance of change, not knowing what will come. As I walk deeper out, I can no longer see the ocean floor. Without a clear view of what is below, my nervous system races, and my imagination runs wild with frightening stories of the sea. I love the feeling of the cool water yet am also aware of the vastness below, with its sea creatures surely present but unknown to me. I am both at peace in the tranquillity of the water and fearful of its apparent emptiness.

Stories have sensationalized this same dilemma, as well as the role of monsters and the vulnerabilities of their prey. Venturing out deeper into the ocean, I bring *The Odyssey* (Homer, 1892) to mind as the soothing water coalesces with the realities lurking at the bottom of the sea. Odysseus's demise is caused by the stingray's deadly venom. My fear of a similar fate is present, yet objectively the water is safe, as I swim with the flow of each wave. I hold both the reality that I am not being harmed and my fears that I may be, both real and not real. Attempting to master my fear, I act like Poseidon maintaining control over the sea. I swim as if, like him, I am the authority of the tide.

The use of storytelling in dramatherapy offers the client the use of narrative to find connections with fables and myth—meanings mirrored in our own lives: "Reassurance is offered by most sacred narratives, precisely because they contain descriptions of an all-encompassing 'once upon a distant time' design and recognize a designer. These sacred narratives, therefore, protect us against the consideration that in the beginning, neither intention nor meaning existed" (Gersie, 1992, p. 225). Dramatherapists approach psychotherapy with the foundational belief that dramatic metaphor, role, and improvisation, among other dramatic principles, provide the basis to explore the world around us and within our psyches. Role theory (Landy, 2007) views life as like theatre with the client as an actor. By exploring roles seen in our everyday life, we can examine our inner conflicts towards psychological healing through role integration.

4.2 Intersections of Dramatherapy and the Hospital Setting

Dramatherapy with anticipatory grief and bereaved children explores actual fears about the illness and dying process. This allows the child to play with both the real and the imagined in the medical centre. Using the tools of improvisation, story, and metaphor, the child and I submerge ourselves in play for the child to understand what death is. The play reminds us to breathe and let go of our impulses to try and control illness and the trajectory of the dying process. Play frees the child to explore their fears of death, and their hopes for life. A child's imagination opens doors to the unknown and possibilities. In *Alice's Adventures in Wonderland* (Carroll, 1865), Alice falls down the rabbit hole to explore her curiosity, landing in a surreal and bizarre place away from reality. Playing about death provides the same portal into a new world. Like Alice, the child's imagination allows an open door to play while simultaneously holding the realities of the situation.

Dramatherapy transcends the realities of the patient's current condition. It allows us to imagine the body in both objective and subjective states (Omens, 2014). Objectively, the body's wellness is measured through interactions the parent or loved one can actually do or not do with the child, due to the illness trajectory. Can they talk to their child, interact, play, and hold them? In tandem with this objective reality, dramatherapy interventions are used to explore the subjective states of what the loved one's body means to the child. A mother may be in the end stages of life. But in the present moment, she is alive. By implementing dramatherapy interventions we can still talk to her and cuddle with her in this physical realm, even if she cannot objectively participate in these interactions. I can speak on behalf of the parent, exploring with the child what their mother would say if she could talk right now. I can incorporate special nicknames that the mother would use to support their special bond. Objectively the parent may not have the strength to hold the child, however, I can create this sense of being held by guiding the parent's arms. Examples of these interventions are explored in greater detail in case studies throughout. Just as theatre emulates real-life scenarios, these are some ways dramatherapy infuses the dramatic processes in the hospital.

Unlike therapy conducted in a traditional therapy room, no "In Session" sign demarcates the sacred space of the therapeutic process. Rather, dramatherapy is conducted within the medical arena. When it is possible, I include the medical team. I introduce the medical team and the child to each other. I encourage the child to ask questions and break down the nurse's answers into language children can understand. Children can be included in the care when appropriate, becoming active in their understanding through participation: not only watching but helping, perhaps holding Dad's hand, or opening a bandage. By knowing what is happening around them, they are playing a part in the care of the parent. Children want to help and be included, to lend a hand in the action rather than being left out, which only adds to their confusion. This is part of the theatrical direction: bringing the child into the hospital drama. Real medical needs are addressed during the imaginative dramatherapy sessions—both coexist, a back-and-forth exchange like the tides. Ideally, the medical staff and I do not behave like rival gangs holding onto our territories. We flow and sway, attempting a harmonious balance.

4.2.1 Drama in the Hospital

In theatre districts, theatres perform different shows nightly. Ritualistically, the actors and audiences prepare in anticipation. Cast members warm up while stagehands set props, the orchestra assembles, and performers adorn themselves with makeup and costumes. When the stage is ready, the lobby lights flash three times. The audience and actors are prepared, and the performance begins.

As in the theatre, life and death in medicine are rehearsed and practiced again and again. As actors are taught to analyze text, rehearse, and finally perform, doctors are taught to see a procedure, perform it, and finally teach it. The expression, "See one, do one, teach one" is familiar to third- and fourth-year medical students during their rotations. Physicians perform operations in a location of the hospital historically known as the "operating theatre." Like actors prepare for performance, the medical team prepares for surgical procedures. The leading actor, the patient, is securely positioned centre stage under bright lights, laid on the operating table. All the supporting actors must be present for this drama to unfold, and they are well rehearsed in their roles. Doctors' surgical equipment must be pre-set just as the props are before a performance. They ceremoniously don their costumes: sterile gowns and gloves. Like the lobby lights flashing three times, a pause signals the beginning of the performance as the surgical team repeats the name of the patient, the surgery to be performed, and the surgical site. Once complete, the operating theatre is ready for the performance and surgery to unfold.

4.2.2 The Hospital in Drama

Audiences have a fascination with horror and gore. The Western theatre canon includes such gruesome classics as Shakespeare's *Macbeth* (1623/2003) and *Titus Andronicus* (1594/2005), Arthur Miller's *The Crucible* (1952), Joseph Kesselring's *Arsenic and Old Lace* (1941), Sarah Kane's *Blasted* (1995), and *Oedipus Rex* (420 B.C.E./2005) by Sophocles. We are drawn to watching real-life situations and exaggerated horrors. Slasher movies both thrill and terrify, compelling viewers to simultaneously watch and shield their gaze. Artists pretend injury and harm in film and on stage, while special effects bring death and near-death dramas to life. In the early 20th century, The Grand Guignol Theatre in Paris produced shockingly real brutality. The performance was so petrifying that spectators often fainted (Hand & Wilson, 2002). In *Le Laboratoire des Hallucinations*, a surgeon unexpectedly discovers that his patient is also his wife's lover ("The Theater," 1947). In a fit of rage, he performs reckless brain surgery. His zombified patient then seeks revenge by gruesomely driving a chisel into the surgeon's brain. Watching these menacing villains chase and kill innocent victims is both thrilling and repulsive. The genre offers catharsis: release through an emotional expression of internal fears.

Children revere animated characters in movies and television. They watch fictional stories, simultaneously believing them both real and not real. They identify and attach to these roles, playing with figures and dolls that represent the cartoons they watch. In play, they can reach into the stories and bring them to life within their imagination Children can both inhabit the character and watch the action unfold from the outside. Harm and injury are played out in animation by theatrical personas like Sylvester the Cat, the Tasmanian Devil, Casper the Friendly Ghost, Road Runner, Bugs Bunny, Marvel heroes, the list goes on. These stories allow catharsis, a place for a child to feel anticipation and relief that the imagined harm is harmless, providing a sense of safety from trauma.

Death and dying are performed repeatedly in the theatre as we attempt to tell stories of illness, injury, and annihilation, striving to understand and master them. In the hospital, I have rehearsed telling and retelling stories of illness as it proceeds toward the end of life. Like the surgeon in the operating theatre conducting procedures on one patient after another, I too have explained death and dying to child after child.

4.3 Intersections of Dramatherapy with Death and Dying

"A time to be born and a time to die."

(King James Bible, 1769/2017, Ecclesiates 3:2)

Death interferes with life. As we go about our daily lives, suddenly there is the onset of illness or a new diagnosis. Traumatic accidents occur in the middle of the day's activities—a father running on a Sunday morning before taking the children to soccer practice is suddenly killed by a car turning a corner. Growing families suddenly stopped, interrupted by death. Yet while managing a life-limiting illness or injury, there are doctors' appointments to make while taking children to school and activities. Babies are born, and birthdays and weddings are to be celebrated. The mail delivers bills, and the mounting cost of medical care cannot be ignored. The daily tasks of life do not yield to illness. Life also interferes with death; medical treatment still proceeds during the dying process.

Likewise, the management of patient care does not stop to make way for dramatherapy. Dramatherapy must find ways to participate in consort with the hospital milieu. My work is not the main task in the dying process. I must stand in the wings waiting for my cue to enter. The sessions I provide occur inside patients' rooms and outside in various areas around the unit. I conduct the dramatherapy sessions at the bedside among the IV poles, respirators, and tubes. Theatre makers move sets, block stage movements, and design scene settings. I have found this training helpful in creating space to work with children in waiting rooms, staff rooms, and hallways. Anywhere I can find, both away from the patient and at the bedside as best meets the needs of the child. In the adult units, there are no designated spaces for children and no appointed space for my sessions.

Children of the dying are not the designated patients; their needs are not billable, and rarely do hospitals create funding for clinicians to do this work. There is also very limited specialized training for therapists in the unique needs of children affected by the death of a parent or loved one. The child's individual needs are underrecognized and often lumped into the caregiver's support. As the body of my work suggests, there is gross neglect in maintaining a high standard of care.

Wherever I find space to work, dramatherapy intercedes, coexisting around and between the interruptions the medical care necessitates. Choreography is needed for the dance to be set in motion. While the medical team is busy providing for the vital needs of the patient they may encounter unusual play worlds, strange and out of place in medical care. Active phases of end-of-life treatment co-occur with children hard at work, learning through play about death.

4.4 Intersections of Myself and the Work

4.4.1 Ethical Considerations

End-of-life and the dying process affect us all differently. Vastly different beliefs become evident when walking into the room of a patient whose trajectory is advancing toward death. Ethical viewpoints, religious practices, and previous experiences all affect our attitudes and behaviors surrounding end-of-life issues. There is a medical definition of death that may differ from religious beliefs. Cultural and spiritual viewpoints are all uniquely held within different social collectives. Subjectively, we each hold our own experience, even when objectively we may be from the same culture, religion, and even within the same family. During a religious service, while everyone is reciting the same prayer, it means something different to each congregant. We all hold our own viewpoints about how and when life ends.

An interdisciplinary team frequently addresses dilemmas about continuing medical interventions and life-sustaining treatments. To this end, rounds and family care meetings include the palliative care and the bioethics teams. Both departments are part of the medical team, integrated to provide guidance on issues of care and quality of life. Bioethics addresses ethical and legal considerations as they arise. The palliative care team provides relief from pain and the best quality of life, no matter the stage of the illness. These supports help guide decision making for the plan of care. When there are children affected, I am included in meetings to advocate for the child's needs.

There are many questions in the exploration between living and dying. I must ask, how can I stay present supporting the child and family, attending to both the living aspects and the death process at the same time? Regardless of my beliefs, my bias, and countertransference based on my own experiences of illness and death, I am in service of the process. I must attempt to expand my awareness of all the complexities, unique to each case. I incorporate religion by asking families about the role of G-d in their lives, their practices around prayer, and what their beliefs are about life and death. I ask what these are even when the religious practice is familiar to me; I do not assume I understand the nuances in each family or even between family members. Each generation may hold different beliefs, this is true between spouses and even between the different sides of the family.

Over the many years, I have encountered variations, but there is always one common thread: the hope for a cure. There is a yearning that whatever the illness is could be stopped. There are prayers for a miracle, be it divine intervention, medical intervention, or magic (as children often believe). No one wants to give up hope. I walk a fine line between speaking the truth and holding hope. I play with the life that is remembered and wished for, but also make a clinical assessment of when to vocalize explicitly, "They will die from this illness." Yet exactly when these words should be spoken—not too early, not too late—is a delicate process. Death cannot be rushed. Yet when it is inevitable, there is a time to confront death in the life of the child.

4.4.2 Tolerating the Intolerable

The life force is strong; there is no mild encounter that ends a life. A tremendous event must occur for a body to die. Death can be slow and incremental, affecting the body's organs in a progressive sequence. As this occurs, it is evident that the activities of daily life gradually diminish as death interferes with the actions of living. Developmental death can be watched, progressing in ways that can be noted. Sudden traumatic injury is very different. Massive force stops life in a single instance, abrupt and final. Without warning, life goes from actively living to inactive. Both causes of death, from illness or injury, are shocking; I privilege neither as more devastating. In either case, I marvel at the sheer power needed to end a life.

It is hard to tolerate witnessing such force. Watching a loved one live with a life-limiting condition is painful. It is very hard to wait the hours, days, weeks, and months leading up to their death. Often we defend against the intolerable by commenting on the treatment decisions of others. It is a misconception that an outside witness can fully understand another's treatment decisions. When a patient is given a plan of care options, privately friends or loved ones often say things like, "I would have … " or "if it were me, I would have chosen a different course of action … " To do so is to stand in the privileged position of not having to make that decision. From the outside, we cannot say, even if we have experienced a similar diagnosis. It is not within our purview to have a subjective discernment of someone's personal experience. Yet, we look for a way to "make it not true." If we can locate the cause by blaming someone or something, we can "solve the problem" by eliminating that variable and returning to the illusion that we are "safe."

This is true of mental illness as well. When it is said that someone died of suicide, people may ask, "Why?" or "What happened?" as if this was sudden and without warning, or a note left will give insight into their action. Often we desire to locate a recent event that can explain such a choice. Yet, it is not possible to comprehend an irrational mental state from an outside, rational perspective. I believe that death by suicide is observable and has an increasingly terminal progression toward death. People tend to see suicidality as the death of one diseased tree in a healthy forest, a single terminal factor that we might compartmentalize. If only this were true, we might excise the decay and heal the tree. In reality, the disease of mental illness often grows and migrates over time, permeating the entire root system of the forest and resulting, finally, in the death of the tree.

I suggest that death by suicide is like death by a life-limiting disease. Both chronic life-limiting diseases and mental illnesses develop and are observable (see Figure 4.1).

In a Western cultural context, we often view cancer as progressive and suicide as a shocking surprise, yet I view them as more similar than they might first appear. As the illness progresses slowly in the body, warning signs may at first be overlooked, misinterpreted as other maladies, or even denied. With severe mental illness, the warning signs of suicidality can likewise be unrecognized. Many people who live with depressive disorders, anxiety, and other forms of mental illness are productive in their professional and personal lives. Very high-functioning individuals are often good at masking their suffering. Loved ones may overlook signs of distress, perhaps as a defensive measure against recognizing the severity of such psychic pain. We have the ability to pretend "as if" everything is okay because our desire is for our loved ones not to suffer. These signs are too hard to watch—unthinkable—and therefore ignored, pushed out of awareness.

I reflect on this from both a clinical perspective and my lived experience. Personally, in my own life, I reflect on my mother's life and choice to end her life by suicide. As a consequence, I had no opportunity to say goodbye. Suicide by whatever means requires powerful and decisive force. Although she ended her own life with one final, sudden action, my mother struggled with living for many years. In truth, her death was both abrupt and a slow progression. Although this could be witnessed, it was never named.

Perhaps this is key to understanding this book. My mother's death drives me to understand the importance of speaking the truth to children, even when the

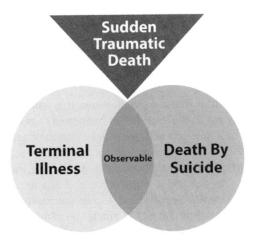

Figure 4.1 Expected versus unexpected end-of-life experiences.

circumstances are complicated and excruciatingly difficult. My mother was beautiful, bright, and accomplished, but also led a very complicated and turbulent life. She was a psychologist who lived much of my life in communes or ashrams pursuing enlightenment. She participated in the counterculture and personal growth movement during the mid-1970s in southern California, often leaving me and my siblings behind.

What would my childhood have been like, had someone explained to me that my mother lacked the capacity to mother? But how do you explain to a child that her mother has chosen not to care for her? Not once, but unfathomably over and over again, she chose to give me away to relatives, friends, and strangers, and ultimately, she chose to die. Again and again, she made the choice to leave. How can one contextualize this for a child? And with this question, is the answer. There *are* words (see "Stephie's Story" on the "Store" tab of my website: https://nowhitelies.com/store or www.routledge.com/9780367461041 under "Support Material") but because they are too painful and at times horrific, we leave them unsaid, causing confusion and separation from the truth. This lack of words isolates a child from family members who collude to withhold the truth. There are some words surrounding my mother's suicide that I do not say, even after three decades, but the story *can* be told and I can tell it. I have lived over three decades since her death, a motherless daughter, and my grief and the story remain. Through my work, I help children say goodbye: to enter the room and see their parent, to hold their hand, say "I love you," and kiss them one last time. These are things I was not able to do. In offering these opportunities, I attempt to understand my own story and stories like mine.

4.4.3 Rushing the Death

Repeatedly I have encountered a phenomenon among families during the end stages of life—be it death resulting from suicide, illness, or injury—which I refer to as "rushing the death." Obviously, coping with loss is an arduous process. During the early, middle, and late phases of the dying process, there are many changes in functioning and engagement. Not only is this true for the dying person, but also for the family. Although loved ones have unique experiences of the dying process, they often share the shock of not expecting the process to last as long as it does. This is also true of the dying person themselves. They express how hard it is to witness the suffering and pain of their children. This wish for suffering to end runs concurrently with the longing for a curative intervention or miracle. Even when the quality of life is poor, the longing to discover a "magic pill" is powerful. If nature does take its course and the individual dies, then suffering ceases and peace is restored. For the dying, there is no more affliction, no more pain. Yet for the living, the grief is ongoing and must be endured.

In my mother's situation, she could literally no longer live with herself and had lost all hope. She could not tolerate the consequences of her actions. The progression of the events leading to this occurred over many years and the string of bad choices was interminable. She was self-righteous in her moral convictions. Without the liberty to live as she chose, she could not deal with the pain and suffering of her life. Therefore she "rushed her death," immediately and finally.

The rushing process in the hospital room is similar. We use defensive measures to escape suffering. In the struggle between attempts to prevent the inevitable, families present false narratives to children. However, the process is not a binary between life and death. It is painful to deal with the liminal space: the complexities of life while dying, and the complexities of dying while being alive. It is a natural response to turn away from what hurts us instinctively. It is human nature to seek comfort and safety. The goal is to attempt to tolerate the discomfort, rather than to push it away in a rush to end suffering.

For most of us, the phases in the dying process are unfamiliar and difficult to watch. As the dying person transitions, there are noticeable changes in their interactions, interests, and appearance. The beloved becomes further detached from their surroundings and responses to others. This is a normal part of the progression to death. These physical changes can be hard to witness, as it can be disturbing to see the marked changes in the body.

Fundamentally we understand ourselves and others by locating ourselves in the objective physical form. Our bodies are what we understand as the self: who we are and our identity (Omens, 2014). The totality of our being is housed within our anatomy. As we watch the objective changes to the body during the dying process, there is a dissonance between who we know our loved ones to be and objectively what we see before us. Just like the dying person turns towards inward reflection and away from interacting with the world around them, we may wish to turn away from the body's changes as the dying process accelerates. These changes cause us to dissociate between the body we had come to know, and what the body has become. We literally cannot associate the person with the body we see. Subjectively, however, we continue to maintain our experience of the body. As a way of defending against this dialectical discrepancy, we rush the process.

This is a projective way for adults to protect themselves against the objective experience they can no longer withstand. The entire family colludes to silence the truth as a defence against fear and suffering. In the false reality that we inflict upon the child, the adult is able to rush through the less tolerable experiences of the dying process. This lying becomes a collective abandonment of the child, leaving them behind in a fog of confusion. Telling the truth would expose how ill-prepared the adult is to deal with the child's needs, to help them handle and understand what is happening. Having been left out of the process, the child is rendered powerless. This powerlessness can often manifest itself in distress later in life that can be traced back to this exclusion.

Chapter 5

Developmental Considerations

5.1 Key Concepts and Theories Explained in Simple and Direct Language for Non-professionals

Children grieve differently from adults. Their grief does not follow the widely accepted Kübler-Ross (1969) model of five stages of grief. In her book, *On Death and Dying*, Kübler-Ross proposed the emotional states individuals experience during the grief process. She described this process in stages: denial, anger, bargaining, depression, and acceptance. Kübler-Ross's model has been criticized (Avis et al., 2021) for being based on reports from the individuals dying and not those affected by the death (Stroebe et al., 2017). In addition, the notion of stages implies a linear progression each needing completion prior to moving on (Bisconti et al., 2004). Kübler-Ross and Kessler (2014) later expanded this model, viewing grief as more fluid, vacillating back-and-forth between feeling states. They revised the phases to not necessarily arrive at acceptance or finally come to a resolution of grief.

Children were not included in the five-phase model and it cannot be assumed to apply to them. A child's experience of grief changes with each developmental stage. We also must consider that not all children meet developmental milestones at a precise age. It is vital to consider basic principles of child development and how this continuum affects the grieving process. Although individual children vary, there are characteristics typical of each stage. This can be confusing to adults; as a child changes and evolves, so does their process of understanding and coping with grief and this cannot be assumed to be regression. Therefore, with children who have experienced loss at a young age and appear to have "managed" well, their expression of grief could resurface during puberty and adolescence in different forms. A child's grief changes as they master greater cognitive ability at every level of development.

However, there are many factors which can contribute to complex grief reactions. These experiences can arise when disruptions in a child's attachment with primary caregivers have occurred before the loss. I acknowledge and have worked with families and children who were already experiencing stress before the illness or acute injury. It is important to identify children with pre-existing

DOI: 10.4324/9781003026938-5

attachment issues. During the intake process, I identify prior experiences of death and other extenuating situations, such as recent divorce, the loss of a pet, or other issues. However, these comorbid issues will not be explored here.

The following stages look at the child's experience and expression as well as their potential understanding of death and the grief experience. Each child is unique. This is a broad guideline towards understanding of how each developmental stage (Erikson, 1950, 1959, 1968; Piaget, 1952) applies to a child's experiences of the world, and therefore death and dying ("A Child's Concept of Death," n.d.; "Children's Understanding of Death," n.d.; Leeuwenburgh & Goldring, 2008; Salek & Ginsburg, 2014).

5.1.1 Infants and Toddlers

In healthy human development, infants and toddlers from birth to age two have strongly established relationships with their parents, family members, and loved ones. Infant bonding begins immediately after birth. Placement on a caregiver's chest, skin-to-skin, keeps the baby's temperature regulated and supports the baby's orientation to their caregiver (Mount, 2022). Infants naturally "root" for a nipple and follow a biological drive to nurse. However, it is essential to note that not all caregivers breast feed, and a healthy bonding process can occur regardless of the caregiver's gender or genetic relationship (Chabat & Balmès, 2010). Jennings (2011) described attachment through play as early as *in utero*. Her work on neuro-dramatic-play (NDP) established play as essential to the unborn child's brain development and fundamental for social and emotional wellbeing, facilitating secure infant attachment. Through play and drama, bonding begins at the start of life.

5.1.1.1 Mothering, But Not Mother

As I stood in the doorway, I watched Max alone in his room. Even though she was not there, it was evident to me that Max had already formed an attachment with his mother. The bond between mother and child was visibly observable in his behavior. Max was swaddled tightly, contained in a little cocoon. His legs twitched and his whole body shuttered from time to time, fighting the tucks and folds of the blanket. I could hear his attachment to his mother in the high-pitched cry, a screeching sound piercing the room. He was born full term weighing 7 lbs 2 oz, with soft brown hair and ten little fingers and toes. Though seemingly perfect, he was admitted to the neonatal intensive care unit (NICU) shortly after birth. His mother had not been to the unit, nor had she held him since he was held within her body, yet it was clear to me that Max was attached to her.

It became apparent to me while working in the NICU that babies form an attachment to their mothers in utero. Babies like Max were born to addicted mothers who continued to use drugs throughout their pregnancies. These babies, while attached in the womb, had essentially been using the drugs as well. Max tested positive for heroin, cocaine, and barbiturates at the time of his birth. Neonatal abstinence syndrome (NAS) babies go through a withdrawal protocol to wean them from these substances.

Of course, all caregivers have a distinct style. However, many behaviors are similar. The archetype of a parent is characterized by many recognizable and typical patterns of behavior (Jung, 1948). Working with Max, I played the archetypal role of mother, as I spent time with him when his mother could not. I held Max to support him weaning off the drugs in his system. I held him to my chest, wrapped snugly in his blanket. I kept one hand on the top of his head. My other hand held his legs tucked up against his bottom. The light was kept low and the sounds reduced to help his agitation. The adage "listen to your gut" is never more clear than while holding a baby. With the lights low and sound reduced, the small feelings and sounds of the baby are amplified. I am listening not only with my ear, but literally feeling the baby's body against mine. Attuning to the baby literally with your gut, you can feel them cry. You can feel their digestive tract: the burps and gurgles as they move through their bodies, easing the discomfort as they pass. I could feel all of this while holding Max: simultaneously holding him literally and, as Winnicott (1960) described, "holding" the therapeutic space. while playing the role he needed throughout his hospital stay.

Infants and toddlers have profound awareness of the changes in their environment. Lacking sophisticated verbal skills, they express their thoughts and feelings through demonstrated behaviours of distress to sudden disruptions in their contact with primary attachment figures. Infants and toddlers adjust over time, even when they experience the sudden death of a parent or loved one. Attachment theory explores early disruptions of attachment figures related to personality development, neurodevelopment, and behaviours later in life (Bosmans et al., 2020; Bowlby, 1988).

5.1.1.2 An Infant Grieves; The Body Remembers

Many years ago, I met one baby in the pediatric emergency room following the sudden, tragic death of her mother. She was 6 months old and survived an automobile accident that killed her mother upon impact, yet left her absolutely unharmed. The nurse asked me to stay with the baby until her father was located and brought to the hospital. She slept peacefully in my arms and I cradled her perfect round head in the palm of my hand. With my fingers I stroked her hair and gazed at her sleeping face. She was beautiful and physically unharmed, in stark contrast to the devastating loss she had suffered. I held the *baby for several hours until her father came. During that time she woke up hungry and the nurse gave me a bottle to feed her. I tickled her lips gently with the bottle's nipple and she opened her mouth, but she would not suck. With milk dribbling down her chin, she thrust out her tongue, struggling to form a seal around the nipple that would allow her to drink. It was immediately clear to me that her mother breastfed her and the baby did not know what to do with the plastic nipple – a shape, texture, and smell that were not her mother and completely unfamiliar to her. I took a deep breath, considering the bond between mother and child, the ache of this trauma manifested in her little mouth and tummy. Empathically, I felt this pain too, the tragedy of this loss for the baby and this young family. Eventually she drank and I could fully exhale, knowing she would survive unimaginable loss. She would be loved deeply by her father and family. Years later I was told that her father remarried and she had younger siblings. The family was happy and growing. This story stays with me, the sad, yet hopeful example of infant attachment and coping with grief and loss, as Dr. Seuss in* Horton Hears a Who *(1954) proclaims, "Because, after all, a person is a person no matter how small."*

5.1.2 Children Three to Five Years Old

When working with toddlers, I use basic, simple language to communicate that a loved one has died and will not come back. Even describing events related to the death can be recounted in terms a young child can understand. I am often questioned about a young child's ability to understand death, loss, and permanency. Even very young children understand peek-a-boo, the concept of "here" and "not here." They also understand when a toy is broken and the joy experienced in having that toy fixed, or the sorrow when it is beyond repair. Some children even have seen a dead bird or animal and understand what that animal looks like and the concept that the bird will not fly again.

Helping children of this age to cope by maintaining their regular routine as closely as possible is extremely important. Keeping familiar items close to them and providing an environment with minimal changes supports their coping. The smell of their loved one's pillow or t-shirt can be soothing to the grieving child. A child can be comforted by photos of their loved one. Drawing and looking at pictures of the deceased can reinforce positive memories and associations to the person who died.

The idea of showing a child photos tends to frighten parents and families. "Won't that make them remember?" I am often asked. A child can never forget a parent or close member of their family who has died. Their memories of their parents, siblings, or an anticipation of a pregnancy cannot be erased, nor should they be. Amy, the infant I held for hours coaxing her to drink, remembered her mother not in words but deeper in her body. She knew and remembered.

Children in this age range have not yet developed abstract thinking, such as the ability to understand concepts like wisdom, freedom, or ideas that are not concretely, physically available to them. Children of this age may become deeply troubled when a favourite teddy bear goes missing behind a blanket, becoming distressed until joyously discovering that the bear, once uncovered, is still there. They will not understand the permanence of death and often ask if or when their loved one will come back. This is true even of older children and can happen long after the death. They will often ask the question and need to be told again that death is permanent and that means the person they love will not come back. This can be very disturbing to the adults. A child I once worked with, after attending a graveside funeral, asked me when his father would come back up from the box under the ground. This child did not mean to unnerve his mother with the question. He was merely attempting to master the concept of where his father's body was and discover an explanation for his absence.

At this age children do not comprehend the events that do not involve them directly. This egocentric way of thinking is a normal part of child development. Magical thinking often results in some children feeling responsible for the death of their loved one, leading children to believe they are omnipotent, that their thoughts or wishes can actually cause events. Believing that the death is connected to them rather than something outside their control, they may also feel rejected and abandoned.

Children three to five years of age need opportunities to play, ask questions, and share memories to process and cope with death. Using honest simple language, they need to take time to talk about the person that died. This can be difficult on the surviving parent, as they may have contradictory needs. While grieving themselves, they may wish to reflect privately. But a child is learning from the adults around them. Parents often think their children are doing well because they are not talking about the loss. However, the parent not speaking about it has taught the child that discussing death is not okay.

The best way to describe death is by stating that the person's body has stopped working, rather than euphemisms. When a child is told, "They've gone to a better place," children have shared with me their profound confusion, asking why the parent would not take them along too if the place was better. A better place for a child is somewhere like Disneyland. Consistent language spoken by all the adults in the child's life can prevent confusion that leads to anxiety. The degree to which children of this age need to be reassured that death is not their fault and their loved one did not want to leave them is not to be underestimated.

Nikky and Kenny's father, whose story I told in Chapter One, shared feedback with me years after his wife died. He said that one of the most important things I had helped him to understand was how much the children needed to hear that they were not responsible for their mother's death. It made a huge difference in their management of the loss. Children need to be reassured that the death is not their fault and their loved one did not want to leave them. Regarding funeral arrangements, children ages three to five years old can benefit tremendously from having a choice about participating. Many parents and grandparents have worried that it will be too sad for other mourners to see young children at a funeral, that they would not be able to understand, or that it will frighten or upset the child. I counsel them, validating that it is tragic when a child's parent dies, but reminding them that everyone attending knows there are young children in the family. Not seeing the children present in no way makes mourners forget that the children are mourning too. Seated in the front row at any funeral are the closest family, in which children can be included. Including them requires preparation for the event, for what they will see, who will be there, and what will take place. They can be included and witness the intensity of the grieving of the adults around them. It helps children to express themselves when they see others expressing emotion. The death of a young parent is sad, and that sadness cannot be diminished. Countless adults have also shared with me that they were not allowed to attend the funerals of a parent, siblings, or loved ones as children and that it remains a source of pain and regret, even into adulthood.

5.1.3 Children Six to Nine Years Old

Children aged six to nine years can begin understanding that death is permanent and that the person will not return. They may have a concept of heaven or some kind of lasting separation and begin to comprehend death more realistically. They may think of death as a character, perhaps an interpretation from a story they read or saw, sometimes even a distorted concept abstracted from Halloween. They imagine "death" as a persona that could take someone away rather than as an event that is part of life's evolution. Children of this age are still very egocentric and are often concerned about their own safety and wellbeing, asking frequently about who will take care of them. At this age their thinking is still concrete, and they struggle to understand what they cannot see, touch, or feel. This may cause them to ask questions, wanting to know specifics about the physical body of their loved one. These questions can sometimes be difficult for adults or feel inappropriate. But knowing and understanding helps children feel more in control and safe.

It is helpful for children to have their questions encouraged and answered in a straightforward, honest, and clear way. By being receptive and open to conversations, adults send the message that even difficult and painful topics can be discussed. Often adults think children cannot overhear them speaking, or that they are not paying attention when conversations are taking place. The opposite is more likely; children are paying very close attention. Children are very smart. When the adults in their lives whisper or talk in hushed voices in another room, this communicates that children are not welcomed to the conversation. Adults might assume that the children are not interested because they are not asking questions, and therefore experience a sense of relief. Children's lack of questions often has more to do with their interpretation that asking questions is not allowed, because no one is encouraging the conversation.

By this age, children understand bodily functions, including the roles different organs and parts of the body play. They can process more details and information about how or why the body is dying or dead. Normalizing details about the process of rigour mortis – such as changes in skin colour or temperature – will help a child's understanding of why and how the body has changed.

5.1.3.1 A Funeral Rehearsed

Gregory was seven years old when his father died from metastatic brain cancer. His father was 44 years old. I had been working with Gregory and his mother for weeks preceding his death. The day before the funeral they came to see me. His mother wanted help exploring with Gregory if he wanted to go to the funeral. She struggled to say the words, overcome at times by her own grief. She asked for my help speaking with her son. She did not know what words to use, how much or how little to explain. If he did wish to attend, she did not know how to prepare him for the church service, open casket, and the many people who were expected to attend.

Gregory was a bright and inquisitive child. During his father's illness and the dying process, Gregory asked many questions, wanting to be informed about the changes during the end-of-life process, and spend time with his father as much as possible. It was not surprising to his mother, or to me, that he very much wanted to attend the funeral. Using a toy box and toy people I talked to him, explaining in clear and simple language that his father's body would be in the front of the church in a box called a coffin. I told him that later that day they would go to a place called a cemetery, where the coffin would be closed and the box lowered into the ground and covered with earth. Gregory watched intently as I used the objects to show him what I was describing. He looked to his mother many times for reassurance, and his mother's face nodded confirming for him this was true.

At one point Gregory stopped and said, "Make this not true." His mother and I both wished that we could grant this, that there would be some way to take it all away. His mother held him tight and I told him that we all wished that, but it was true. I laid down on the ground and told him that the body would be cold and a different color. I explained that when he touched my and his mother's skin, our arms felt warm and soft, but that this would be different tomorrow if he touched his father's body. We talked about the people who would be there, some that he would know and some that he would not know, and gave him permission to speak, hug, or not whenever he wanted.

He told his mother he wanted to touch and kiss his dad. His mother told him that before anyone else came, they would have time alone to do that, if he wanted. It was heartbreaking to watch Gregory cradled in his mother's arms rocking gently, as tears fell down her cheek, wetting his hair. Heartbreaking were the sounds of his crying, and I wished I could, as Gregory requested, make it not true.

The next time I saw Gregory and his mother, he was very excited to tell me all about the funeral and to tell me what it had been like. His mother shared that just as Gregory had played with me and the toys the day before the funeral, she watched him repeat. As if, she said, he was replaying what he'd rehearsed. I knew this was in fact true.

5.1.4 Children Ten to Twelve Years Old

As abstract thinkers, children in this age group begin to develop a more sophisticated understanding of death. They know that death is a part of life and that everything living will die someday. Some children in this stage of development even have a sense of their own mortality. They often ask about how the person died and show an interest about what happens to the body. These sometimes graphic questions may be unnerving for adults and perceived as inappropriate, but they reflect the child's normative developmental need to master the concepts of death and dying. Preteens are often developing a sense of mortality, coupled with their emerging desire to control themselves and their environment. They may perceive death as a punishment.

5.1.4.1 Harrison's Story

Harrison was 11 years old when his father died. His mother called to make the appointment a week after the funeral, telling me Harrison had been sent home from school the previous day for fighting with another child. She said that since the funeral, Harrison had been very angry. I had worked with him during his father's hospital stay and told her I would be happy to see him. As he walked towards my office he remained a few steps behind his mother, not looking at her as he entered my office. He seemed angry to me, but there were deeper feelings to explore underneath his exterior. We arranged some pillows on the floor and sat facing one another. He told me he was mad at his father for dying and about the things people said about him at the funeral. His dad had been a strong man, tall with broad shoulders, a captain in the fire department. His father was a first responder on September 11, 2001, and known as a hero among his community and to Harrison. He had coached little league and football since Harrison was young. Harrison had a special relationship with his father, and I could see how badly he was hurting. He told me about the funeral and going back to school, and how he felt awkward because everyone knew his dad had died. He shared about all the relatives and friends at the funeral. "There were so many people from the firehouse and town. The room seemed to be overflowing," he described, adding that people came up to him talking about his dad and he

didn't like it. "Everyone who spoke said my dad had battled cancer, he fought hard and finally the cancer won." He could not understand this; his father was the strongest person he knew. He had saved people during 9/11, he had been a quarterback when he was in high school and college. There was no way his father could lose a fight against anything or anyone. "Why didn't he just fight harder?" Harrison asked me as tears filled his eyes. "If he had only been stronger and fought harder, then he would still be alive." His anger fell away, allowing for deep sadness.

The perspective that someone living with cancer is a victim fighting for their life implies total powerlessness. Their death becomes a result of losing that fight: their weakness. Cancer is cast as the perpetrator, the individual with cancer the victim. During a robbery the perpetrator has the intent to harm. All efforts on the part of the victim are to protect and to survive the attack. The perpetrator is an outside force whose objective is to inflict harm. The perpetrator holds all the power, rendering their victim helpless. The natural response to danger is fight, flight, or freeze.

The illness is dangerously harmful, but the perpetrator is not an outside force. In the "war" against cancer the assailant is within the body, thus inflicting harm from the inside. This makes it harder to accept. During advanced cases of cancer, leading to metastatic disease, cancer breaks away from its original occupied organ, violating the borders and advances throughout the body, taking on more territory as the battle wages on. Losing assumes surrender. This language does not empower those affected by cancer but suggests they succumb to it and fail.

To me, this conventional language is born out of the need to attribute blame. If there is someone or something to blame, then there is something to fight against, and hope that we can prevail against the harmful element. I have heard many times the words Harrison heard and witnessed families who directed their anger not only at the cancer (#fuckcancer) but also on the medical team (see Figure 5.1).

When words of war against cancer are spoken, is the anger towards the individual? Perhaps the anger is against what cannot be accepted and cannot be controlled. The source of Harrison's anger stemmed from the idea that his father was not strong enough and had given up.

"Your father was not weak, did not lose, nor was he beaten." I explained to Harrison. "He was strong. He would never give up. He wanted to live. He didn't want to die but it wasn't something he could fight his way out of. There was nothing he did wrong to get cancer and nothing he could have done to stop it." This is the very hardest thing, acceptance. Succumbing to acceptance does not mean giving up or becoming a victim.

Because children of this age have a greater ability to express thoughts and feelings, the adults in their lives can explore and clarify their understanding of death. At this age they may have the interest and maturity to participate in some of the funeral planning. Some children even wish to speak and play more active roles during the service.

Figure 5.1 Developmentally appropriate representation of blame from *About the Baby* (Omens, 2017).

With preteens, it is important to emphasize that no one could have prevented the death and that death is not a punishment. This can be hard for adults, who may question this themselves, bargaining for a cause or reason as they struggle to accept the loss. It is helpful to simply state that this was no one's fault, that no one wanted this to happen, and that no one could do anything to stop or cause this. As is true for younger children, open expressions of grief can help the child feel closer and included in the family's mourning process. These shared experiences and the parents modelling of their own feelings creates a shared emotional experience and helps the family during this difficult time. It is also true that the grieving adult needs their own support during this time and they should not rely on the child to help them process by overwhelming the child with their own grief.

5.1.5 Children 13 to 18 Years Old

By adolescence, teens have usually developed a full understanding of death. They may have also begun to integrate concepts of spirituality, perhaps in keeping with the family or diverging. They can understand abstract concepts and conceptualize death and dying in a more sophisticated manner. Adolescents have the capacity to understand moral behaviour, a sense of right and wrong, as well as metalevel processing and reflecting on their own actions. In many areas of their lives, teens are testing boundaries, taking risks, and exploring the limits of their behaviours. The death of a loved one during adolescence can shatter a teen's sense of safety and immortality. They can become overwhelmed with the realization the world they once viewed as within their control is unstable and impermanent.

Adolescence is a time of independence and differentiation from parents or carers. Teenagers may distance themselves, denying the impact of the death, and in some cases avoiding conversations. As with younger children, a parent's ability to model sharing their own feelings gives the teen an invitation to express emotions themselves. Choices about involving them in funeral arrangements can give teenagers the opportunity to participate in their own way and at their own pace. This fosters the teen's development, independence, and autonomy. This may result in a teen's decision not to contribute or even attend. As with children of all ages, it is important to respect and support their decisions. Parental regard for an adolescent's feelings and decision-making abilities strengthens a growing sense of independence and emerging identity.

Finding time to speak casually, in a relaxed manner and without a sense of urgency, can be a helpful way to encourage conversation with teenagers. Keep in mind that some of the most meaningful discussions can be brief. Adults can maintain a relaxed, normalized stance, while encouraging the adolescent's ideas and suggestions about their loved one. This includes exploring how to memorialize that person in a way that is meaningful to the teenager.

5.1.6 Compounded and Traumatic Grief

Previous experiences with loss create complicated grief responses. Multiple losses at one time, or several in a brief time, complicate a child's responses and reactions to the loss. Sudden death, unexpected death, and death by suicide are complex circumstances. In tandem with a child's caregivers' complex grief experiences, both caregiver and child attempt to navigate these complexities. The child's needs may become further complicated by the compounded grief of the adults around them.

Every child responds differently. Often these differences are seen between siblings. When one child is displaying a certain grief response and their sibling another, they both require individual responses from the adults in their lives. Sometimes caregivers feel they must do this alone, balancing both their needs and the child's. When this becomes hard to navigate, the therapist is able to support the grieving process with more objectivity and distance.

It is common to see changes in a child or young person's sleep patterns. These might include difficulty sleeping and seeking reassurance at bedtime or in the middle of the night. Allowing for these changes is recommended. Siblings wanting to sleep in the same room, or perhaps coming into their parents' room to find security during the night, is an appropriate response. Children need reassurance that they will be taken care of and are safe no matter what. It is very common for a child to explore this during night-time.

Similarly, changes in play or activities are typical. Children who were once very tolerant may become easily frustrated. Children who were outgoing before the loss and often took risks may become more cautious and less spontaneous or imaginative while playing. Play is how children express and understand the world. Themes surrounding death and dying are common and should not cause alarm. Many children will play and replay events of the death, which can be alarming to the adults, but is healthy for children who are trying to make meaning of their experience through their play.

A child may seem to behave altogether differently. Changes in mood or ability to regulate emotions may become evident. Children may have a difficult time separating from the closest adult in their lives. It is normal for children to need to be reassured that the surviving adults are not going to die too, as in Nikky and Kenny's story when their father needed to reassure them often that he did not have cancer and was there to take care of them.

Returning back to school after a death is a complex time. Some children worry if their friends, classmates, and teachers know. Explaining the loss to others can overwhelm a child and it helps for an adult to do this for them. Adults transparently telling the child after talking to their school is equally important. School principals and teachers can also use guidance about how much to tell classmates and discuss things other children can do or say to the grieving child. Having the child's teacher or principal send a condolence card signed on behalf of their classmates, or having the classmates sign one themselves, can support a child's awareness that they are loved and cared for at their school. Even if the child does not wish to talk directly about their loss when going back to school, saying nothing can exacerbate a child's feeling different and isolated during the school day. It's helpful to have the principal explain that by saying, "I'm sorry for your loss" or "I'm glad you're back. We missed you" are appropriate things for children to say to a grieving peer. Likewise, adults can help the child prepare to respond to condolences by saying simply "Thank you." It is not uncommon for children to be embarrassed and confused about having people know about the loss. It is important to validate these feelings and to reassure them that their community cares about them.

5.1.6.1 Not Very Helpful

ॐ

When Matt went back to school after the death of his younger brother, he was invited to the school guidance counsellor to talk. Matt was a nine-year-old boy I had worked with during the many months while his younger brother was in the PICU. Throughout our work, I had helped him to understand his brother's illness and supported this understanding as his sibling's condition worsened and during the end of life process. I helped him to express his feelings and prepare for and participate in the funeral. Matt was an expressive and creative child who was profoundly sad and very close to his brother. He was also very clear about what he felt and articulate. His mother called me after she had picked him up from his first day back to school, and Matt asked to come back and meet with me. Matt explained to his mother that when the school counsellor talked to him, she just cried and that it wasn't very helpful.

Stories like Matt's highlight the importance of seeking help from a therapist who specializes in grief with families and children.

5.2 Speaking Truth in Practice: Grief in the Language of Children

I have encountered countless very caring and compassionate people who have said absurd things to children anticipating or having suffered the death of a loved one. Confronting the stark reality of death, especially when a young person or child dies, is unthinkably sad. Most adults have experienced loss and often have a complicated relationship with the experience: wanting to be there when their own grandparent died years ago, or memories from their own childhood of a relative, perhaps even the death of a sibling or parent at a young age. Support groups and therapists specializing in patients coping with illness are abundant, but there is little focus on the children of these patients. Even psychotherapists often do not feel comfortable in this area.

For therapists to speak the unspeakable, to talk to children about life-limiting illness and the end-of-life trajectory, it is important that they recognize their own prior experiences with death. It is essential to acknowledge how one's own experiences have framed preconceptions about talking to children. The more therapists and hospital staff are aware of these effects, the better able we are to support the child before us.

Many adults use indirect communication. As previously discussed, euphemisms like "gone to a better place," "they're sleeping," or "they've passed on" are commonly used. Because children think literally, words intended to protect them can lead to misunderstanding and fear. For example, a child who is told that death is like sleeping may begin to fear going to bed at night. The word "passing" is associated with passing the salt, passing a ball, or passing gas. Being told their sister "passed away" is confusing and unclear to a young child. None of those indirect forms of communication explain what "dead" is.

5.2.1 Wings of the Angel

Her mother brought her to the appointment straight from St. John Paul II Catholic School, still wearing her school uniform, Anne, 11 years old, came

into my office. Her brother had died the week before in the PICU and that was where I had first met Anne. I helped her to understand why her brother was there, how the doctors had tried to make him better, and how to say goodbye to him when he died. As we sat together and talked, Anne told me how sad she was, but that she was not supposed to cry. When I asked her why, Anne shared that when she cried in school, her teacher said she should not cry – that her tears would dampen the wings of the angels and therefore her brother's wings would become wet and he would be unable to reach heaven. I explained to Anne that having sad feelings when someone we love dies is normal, that trying to hold back her tears must feel very hard to do, and that expressing her sadness would not stop her brother from reaching heaven. Ethically I took care that my words aligned with the religious beliefs of Anne's family. I explore with children what they think heaven and angels might look like. I endorse the child's faith while simultaneously considering what can be imagined and what can actually be seen. I can only assume Anne's expression of sadness made the teacher feel uncomfortable. Yet the teacher's feelings were not Anne's responsibility. Without intending to, Anne's teacher gave her an unbearable burden. By suggesting that crying would prevent Anne's brother's soul from reaching heaven, the teacher insinuated Anne's responsibility for his spiritual afterlife and that Anne's grief showed contempt for G-d. Anne deeply respected her teacher and believed in the lessons she learned at school. Thus in a tragic conflict, Anne became torn between her grief and her faith, a double bind creating great psychological stress.

Wherever possible, I create a special place to speak with children. As previously discussed, I choose the staging for these conversations with intention. I work with the primary caregivers when choosing whom to invite and who not to include in the conversation. Family members are, of course, grieving themselves. A child's grandparents are facing the death of their child. Yet additional people in the room, in their anxiety, will often derail the conversation away from communicating the main objective. The focus of this conversation is on the child: their understanding and their expression of emotions.

Often limitations prevent finding a space that is appropriate for such a difficult conversation. I have delivered "bad news" in locker rooms, break rooms, hallways, alcoves, unoccupied offices, and waiting rooms. While such spaces are not therapeutic, nor devised with the child in mind, these rooms and the people in them will be remembered by the child forever. In this room, the child will experience being told that a parent or sibling is dead or that they will not survive.

There are objects, sounds, and smells forever imprinted in the mind. People often say, "I don't like hospitals" because they have associations between the sensory elements of the hospital environment and difficult times in their lives. Special care and thought for children and a child's receiving of bad news can make all the difference in a child's overall coping.

When I am consulted, my first meeting is not with the child, but with the parents or caregivers. During this meeting, I assess the family's needs. I offer space for them to ask questions they may have and to share their fears and concerns. While counselling the family, I am also educating them about my suggestions and recommendations. With their consent, I have the opportunity to understand the values of the family, their beliefs about death and dying, and how they see this affecting their children.

I include the parents to the degree they wish to be included. Some parents want to be more active in sharing the information with their children, and some ask me to speak these difficult, unspeakable words for them. Although I promote and encourage the words to come from the family, I am most often asked to speak for them. That's okay; I have said these words many times before. I am modelling for the family what language to use. My interactions with the grieving child are often limited, but the family will continue to support conversations at home. I want to demonstrate and share with them how they too can continue talking to their child long after this meeting.

I use an open, honest, and straightforward tone and approach when speaking with children. I get down on the floor or at eye level when possible to create and support connection. I let the child know that this conversation is special and scheduled just for them. This lets children know they are a priority and heightens the importance of the discussion. I take my time and listen, trying to limit distractions and interruptions. I incorporate any important beliefs or cultural values while supporting the child's developmental understanding. I organize the chairs in the room so that the family is near the child to provide comfort and support. When possible, I incorporate members of the medical team. This conveys to children that we are all on the same page and that there are no secrets. It is also helpful for children to be able to directly ask medical questions to providers. These conversations are hard and emotional. Crying is natural and I expect this. Often children look to their parents, watching their parents' emotional expression, which gives them permission also to express themselves.

5.2.2 Too Young to Understand

A neurosurgeon had just conducted the second and final declaration of brain death on his patient, a 42-year-old father of two young children. The patient's wife had asked for help explaining this to her two children and I had been called to the unit. As the doctor exited the room, I was introduced and the nurse told him the patient's wife had requested help. The doctor was dismissive and told me that, since the children were too young to understand, he had previously told the patient's wife just to tell them their father was sleeping. But when someone is sleeping, he wakes up to his wife and children calling his name. I told the surgeon that this kind of advice was not

recommended but if he would refrain from offering well-meaning, though inaccurate, advice for children, I would stay away from the operating room.

Working as a member of a multidisciplinary team, I ask members of the medical professions to tell me about the patient's condition, the plan of care, and expectations. I assess the needs for the child within the medical model. When families have questions about medical details, I defer to the medical team. My job is to interpret this information in a language children will understand, breaking down complex concepts and assembling these in the world of the child.

5.2.3 Is There Another Word?

Lucy was eight years old. She and her mother lived with her mother's parents. She did not know her father. Lucy's grandparents would continue to care for her after her mother died. She understood quite a lot about her mother's illness. She knew it was called cancer, about the surgeries her mother had, and she had seen the hair loss. She had also watched her mother become weaker, not able to take Lucy to school or pick her up. She was unable to do so many things, having become weak as her mother's cancer metastasized and the treatments failed. Her oncologist had recommended hospice and palliative care a few weeks before. When the pain became too much to handle at home, her mother came to the hospital.

Lucy's mother was no longer able to get up, eat, or interact. She was receiving pain medicines to make her comfortable. She was actively dying. Lucy's grandparents were aware they would have to explain to Lucy that her mother was not coming home and did not know how to say this to their grandchild. I was called to speak with them privately. Lucy was not with them, she was in the waiting room with her aunt. While speaking to me, her grandparents asked what words to use to explain to their granddaughter that her mother would "pass." I explained how direct, honest, and developmentally appropriate words would help Lucy understand that her mother was not getting better and would die from cancer. "Passing" is interpreted by a child to mean the moving of an object from one place to another, I explained to them. Children think in concrete terms; they are very literal in their understanding. Her grandparents listened and cried while we spoke. They were losing their daughter and they grieved not only for her but also for their granddaughter and themselves. This kind of loss is very hard on grandparents: experiencing both the death of their child and their sadness and concern for their grandchildren, their grief is layered. I told them the words I recommended: "She will die from cancer. There is no more medicine to make her better. The doctors and nurses have tried everything, but her mother's body is stopping and she will die." Her grandfather asked if there was another word, other than "dead" – a softer, nicer word. I asked what word that would be. "Move on?" he suggested. I asked him: Where did she move to? And why couldn't Lucy move there too? We talked through other suggestions. Gone with G-d? With the angels? Called to heaven, crossed over? To each I asked about the location of these places, and emphasized the confusion this would create.

Incorporating concepts of G-d, heaven, and angels are all a part of my work, if they are within the religious beliefs of the family. I explore these and can integrate them into the child's understanding. This, however, entails separating the *physical, objective understanding* of the body from the *thoughts* about the parents or siblings: the child's subjective understanding, feelings, and experience of the person who is dying (see Omens, 2014).

I use the terms *objective* and *subjective* theoretically to refer to the actual body and how objectively the body changes during the illness process, separate from the emotional, felt a sense of the person. The objective refers to the physical, real sense of the body, the concrete and observable states of wellness or unwellness. When working with children, I address the physical body. In Lucy's story, this meant discussing how thin her mother had gotten, that her mother's eyes were shut and she was breathing slowly in an irregular pattern. Her grandparents understood and asked me to meet with Lucy. I asked Lucy to tell me what she observed, the changes that she saw, so that I could further explain them. I speak about these things not to be harsh or abrasive, but to name the unnameable, to speak what is unspeakable, and help the child understand what was previously not understood.

But about concepts that cannot be seen, that are felt or core beliefs? I am often asked, "What about G-d?" How do I incorporate religious beliefs? These beliefs are subjective to each person, and I ask each family what they believe. These are subjective realities which I use to support the child's internalized sense of their loved one. These subjective thoughts, feelings, and memories, exist outside of the objective truths about the body. They exist in the mind. Embodiment is a subjective experience unique to each of us – not the physical feel of the body, but the emotional and lived sense of the body. I ask children what makes their Mommy special. What games does she play with you? What foods does she cook? What is the special nickname she calls you? I ask children where they feel love and they will tell me inside, in their hearts. This is not the anatomically correct heart, which I might show in an illustration to explain how it is no longer beating. Rather this is the symbolic heart which contains the loving feeling of arms wrapped around them, bedtime stories read over and over again, wishes of the sweetest of dreams and kisses goodnight (Figure 5.2).

It is in this subjective portrait of Lucy's mother that I come to understand who this mother is to her child: what Lucy loves about her mother, the places they went together, and the things that they did that were fun and silly. I collected these stories from Lucy. I asked her if she could feel her mother's love,

Figure 5.2 Illustration of predictability and safety from *About Cancer* (Omens, 2017).

even though her mother could not say the words, "I love you." Did Lucy know her mother loves her? I knew she would say yes. I described clear and objective truths about her mother's body and what this meant. She told me all the ways that she knew her mother's love and how this love is with her. This is where we speak of G-d, spirit, and soul. When it is said, "The spirit is still with you," a child can understand the spirit as stories, photos, and memories, and I will help them understand this through the use of play.

Play is the predominant modality for a dramatherapist. But how do you play with death and dying? The concept of play provides an opportunity to learn about a family's history through stories. These stories allow me to build a rapport and the means to create a non-threatening atmosphere for children and parents to grieve together as a family. I find opportunities to create action-oriented ways for children to interact, explore, and process the grieving process through creative means. Milestones, such as religious holidays and birthdays, can continue to be celebrated. Rituals such as creating a birthday party to honour the life of a loved one may seem like an odd approach. Yet bringing in elements of play allows an opportunity for imaginative play with their parents following a death. This playful space, the room transformed from reality into a world the children can imagine, provides normalcy and encourages imagination.

Play can be a non-verbal form of communication, a way to express feelings when a child may not have the words during an unimaginable situation. Even in a moment that feels devoid of possibility, playful self-expression can comfort and provide healing. In play there remains spontaneity and the possibility of what to create.

Chapter 6

Tangled Web of Lies

6.1 Truth-telling: The Training of the Lie as Projective Resistance for the Caregiver

6.1.1 Lies to Survive

In May of 1940, the Germans invaded the Netherlands. In 1942, at the age of five, a young girl was sent away by her courageous parents to be placed in the care of others. Her parents had the foresight to know that hiding their child was the only chance for her survival. I spoke with this child, now a grown woman with children and grandchildren. She had many stories to tell from the 80 years since being separated from her parents. But the story I tell here takes place after the end of the war, after she was reunited with her father and they came to America. Her mother did not survive the concentration camp in which she was murdered along with many family members.

The 86-year-old woman talked to me about the lifetime of lies she feels she's lived, and how the difference between truth and lies meant her survival. She discussed how even today, those lies still affect her. She does not remember being sent away by her loving parents, or if she was told anything about being sent away to live with strangers. She played a game of calling these new people her family. She was instructed to lie, to call these people Momma and Poppa, others Aunt and Uncle. Maintaining the lie was her survival: the discrepancy of denying her identity while missing her parents deeply. It was hard for her to remember to maintain the lie and she made mistakes. When she forgot, she was punished abusively. She was hungry and stole food, apples she picked from trees in a neighbor's garden. She ate any food she could find. She was always hungry. When the missing food, plucked apples, or bits of bread were discovered missing, she lied. Lied that she did not take the food and lied that she was not hungry. She became sick and lied that she felt well. Her life depended on these lies. She lied to survive.

Her father survived the camps and they moved to live with family in New York City. She was ten years old and remembers sitting with her father, while

DOI: 10.4324/9781003026938-6

he lay sick in bed. She was not told he had cancer, or why he was ill. The truth was omitted. He told her stories of the places they would travel and visit when he got well. He offered elaborate descriptions of the cities they would visit and things they would do together as soon as he felt better. She believed him and looked forward to their adventures together, waiting for the day he would get stronger and fulfil his promises.

One day she was sent off to school and when she came back, he was gone. Her relatives told her he merely went away, nothing more was explained. She believed what she was told and never imagined it was a lie. She could not believe he was not coming back to take her away as he had promised.

It was a school friend who told her the truth. The friend asked, "Who died at your house?" This was the first time she heard that her father died. She felt betrayed and angry, wondering why he would lie to her. She had no idea what her aunt meant when she explained that her father had "Gone away to heaven." She was not taken to his funeral. Her aunt had wanted to spare the child.

She now reports that at the time it felt to her as if her "arm had been cut off." A forever missing limb, a series of lies – some that saved her, some that wounded her forever. The woman wondered aloud, was her whole life a lie?

In an attempt to protect their children and to decrease their own suffering, adults disguise the truth. "Passing on" or "passed away." "They didn't make it." "Gone to another place." "Gone to a final resting place." "Called to G-d, to heaven, to a better place," or "called home." "Transitioned," or "moved on." "Crossed over." These euphemisms, indirect and evasive, are used to protect and soften the meaning of death. They are half truths, lies by omission – little white lies, because the truth seems too harsh or too blunt. This indirect language is spoken well meaningly, not intended to be harmful. Families are trying to do the right thing by shielding their children from pain. But exactly who they are trying to shield becomes confused. Their attempts to keep the grief at bay merge with their own inability to tolerate witnessing the grieving child. The adults are also in disbelief; their wife, husband, or grown child will not survive. The family must not only manage their own devastating loss but also that of the children. They want so badly for reality to be altered. It is as if by not saying the truth, by not using clear and direct words, the death could become disguised – as if the adults could hide the truth not only from the child, but also from themselves.

Nikky and Kenny's story, described in Chapter 1, is unusual. More common are the parents who contact me only when there is little hope for survival and the need to speak with the children is unavoidable. I have many of these stories:

A father whose wife died told his young children that their mother was never coming home again. However, no other explanation was given. I suggested the need to clarify where it was that she actually went and why she could not come home, that she had died, and to explain to them what "dead" means. He told me that the children were not asking anything about her, and therefore he felt they were doing well and no further conversation was needed.

A pregnant mother who in her last trimester no longer felt the baby moving was admitted to the hospital. Her baby was stillborn. She felt it would be best not to discuss this with her 3-year-old daughter, that the child would simply forget. She and her husband planned to be pregnant again soon, so they felt she would not notice.

A woman receiving chemotherapy felt if she wore a wig and never let her children know about her hair loss, she would not need to tell them she had cancer or about her cancer treatment.

A father receiving weekly chemotherapy treatment explained his leaving the house frequently as "trips to the store," and told his children the medication on the counter was his vitamins.

Double mastectomies are explained as back pain. Cancer is described as a cold. Nausea from medication became a meal that did not agree with them. The rationalizations I have heard and the frequency with which I have heard them are endless.

When faced with these unthinkable truths, many parents attempt to protect *themselves* by not telling their children. Adults are concerned the children will have an emotional reaction visiting the hospital, with the knowledge that their sibling or parent will die and wanting to say goodbye. Seeing a child cry is difficult to watch. It is very sad and there is no way to solve or fix this for the child. In normal situations, the source of a child's tears – falling from a bike, the end of a play date, not getting another cookie, a balloon string let go of and floating away – these tears are easily soothed. No one wants to see a child suffer. Grandparents might try to distract the child, by offering snacks or a toy. Some may even tell the child not to cry.

6.1.2 Nothing More to Say

"When someone dies their body stops and then can't come back to life. She is dead." After I spoke, I looked at Vivian and said nothing. There was nothing more to say at the moment. I kept my gaze upon her as she looked to her father and grandmother as if searching for an alternative to the awful truth that she just heard. They all sat silently, crying. I watched as her face changed, she turned pale, and tears streamed down her cheeks. A sound came from deep down inside of her, a wailing and screaming that moved up and out. The room and the hallway filled with the sound of a child's heartbreak. It was loud and became louder as she rocked back and forth. As if trying to crawl away from her body, away from this place and from the truth. Her father opened his arms wide, drew her into his lap, and wrapped her in a cocoon, rocking her. She continued to cry, loudly and without relenting. Of course there was

no consoling her. No one could take the pain and loss away. The child's cry was a clear reminder that this situation was not solvable. I sat breathing deeply while the family looked to me beseechingly as if I could stop this, as if I had the power to stop her pain. To make it stop. Simply, I could not. I only had the power to witness this pain and remain present for her.

Time passed and she would ask me many times if this was true. She asked in many ways, both with questions and with her eyes, searching for a way out of this truth. I asked Vivian if she was ready to see her mother. She was, but was unable to walk, her legs weak, her body shaking in shock as she crumbled when standing, having lost the will to move. She only had the power to cry and she did. She continued to cry.

As we moved from the room, down the hallways toward the ICU, Vivian continued to be unable to walk, and I got her a wheelchair and wrapped her in a blanket. She slumped like a rag doll and continued crying, visitors and staff looking on. It was clear to see the source of her tears was not physical. It was the sight and sound of grief. As we stood to wait for an elevator, Vivian's father leaned near to me and asked, "Can we give her medication to sedate her?" I explained there was no medication to give her, that this emotion was appropriate to the information she was given. The love and loss were as huge and as loud as the reason for her tears.

I remembered a time when I cried like Vivian, lost in grief: wailing, moaning, rocking, blind with tears. I could not see past the all-encompassing sorrow, could not comprehend the room or the world, completely consumed with grief. I cried like that when I heard my mother died. I cried all night, writhing in pain upon hearing the words. I can still remember the sound of the phone ringing and my brother's voice. I knew what he was about to say, sensed it before the words were spoken. His voice was different, and I knew what he had to say was horrible and true. There was no lead-up to her death, no slow progression of physical illness. No spoken diagnosis. It was not cancer. Her suicide was a shocking, dark, forbidden death. My cry in horror was the immediate and appropriate response in the aftermath of her death.

Crying is something I expect. It is sad and healthy to have emotions appropriate to the situation. Injury and illness are the causes of death, not feelings and emotional expression. Parents want to protect their children from their sadness. Witnessing grief is difficult to tolerate. There is a desire to push it away when we see others' sorrow, as the sorrow we have experienced in our own lives comes rising up. But to be able to identify with the child's sadness without letting it overwhelm you, tolerating it without over-identifying with it, communicates that to the child they are not alone. That you are with them in their sadness: you see it, acknowledge it, and can tolerate their pain. This is a gift.

The converse response was the reaction of Vivian's father – the desire to medicate her pain away, to stop her expression and therefore decrease the outward expression of his own internal experience. I use this example because it is representative of so many more. The desire to spare the child pain coupled with the parent's own pain becomes too great to bear.

No young family is prepared for these conversations. Compounded by learned discomfort around the whole topic, guidance is not easily found. Parents who are caregivers often turn to a grandparent, extended family member, or medical staff, who in turn are struggling with the truth themselves. Additionally, talking about death to children is not an area that many therapists feel comfortable with or specialize in, making support more difficult to find. The uncomfortable topic combined with the lack of resources makes it much easier to turn away from the truth.

Often young families are given misleading advice by family and friends. However well-meaning this advice is, it is often not what I would recommend. Mostly these suggestions can create more confusion for children. White lies, omissions, and euphemisms, create confusion, increase a child's fear, and lead to mistrust. The child often fills in the missing pieces, which compounds their anxiety and stress. In the adults' wish to protect the children from all harm, more harm is created, because they tell a lie.

6.2 Deconstructing the Lie: Unsticking the Grief

6.2.1 "White Lies"

What is the meaning of a "white lie?" A "little white lie" is a deception often thought to have little importance and told to prevent harm. A lie, by contrast, is the telling of a falsehood with the *intent* to deceive. How does such a falsehood, with the simple addition of "white," become innocent? While some sources deny the link between this phrase and racial connotations (DiNuzzo, 2021; Perlman, 2018), it is difficult to conceive of separating notions of whiteness from purity, innocence, and goodness Hart (2020). In studies of participants' unconscious associations between whiteness and morality and blackness and immorality, Sherman and Core (2009) concluded that "that ideas about purity and pollution are central to seeing morality in black and white" (p. 1019). For example, the authors cited the symbol of the white wedding dress to denote moral purity. This "pure" white is easily "blemished" by a drop of darker colour. We cannot escape these connotations in the phrase "white lie."

Just as the notion of associating purity and whiteness harmfully perpetuates implicit notions of racial purity, I argue that the "white lie" is not benign at all. Rather, it is an oxymoron. This evokes similar terms that are used all too frequently: "disinformation," "alternative facts," "fake news." All are falsely told with intent and, when deconstructed, contain those components outlined earlier. As Berthold wrote, "everyday 'purity ideals' bite their own tails, that is, they undermine idealists professed purpose in concrete ways" (Berthold, 2010, p. 2). These "white lies" that appear to be innocuous can often do harm that takes a lifetime to untangle. The teller of the lie knows it to be untrue but intends it to be kinder than the truth. In *A Few Good Men* (1992), Jack Nicholson famously shouts, "You can't handle the truth!" aggressively implying that he withholds the truth because it will not be accepted. Yet children *can* handle the truth about death and dying.

Intertwined with connotations of morality and immorality, or "goodness" and "badness," in the phrase "no white lie," is the implicit metaphor of stark contrasting colours. The contrast between black and white signifies there is no mistaking one from the other. Night and day, sunlight and darkness are clear delineations and unavoidably different from each other. As Hermia described in *A Midsummer Night's Dream* (Shakespeare, 1600/2011), the night obscures what we see, leaving us to imagine based on what clues we can hear:

> Dark night, that from the eye his function takes,
> The ear more quick of apprehension makes.
> Wherein it doth impair the seeing sense,
> It pays the hearing double recompense. (3.2.177–180)

The lie is rationalized as a kindness because the stakes are seen as low and "harmless," yet the reality can be much more dangerous. Just like for Hermia, what is unseen creates the desire to discover the truth. In the short term, the lie appears to have solved the problem. Yet its harmful effects emerge long into the future. In my clinical experience, adults who were lied to as children often later reflect on their anger and sadness at not being told the truth. Conversely, children I worked with during the moment of trauma have reflected to me years later about the benefits of being told the true story of what happened (see "Brother Toy" in Chapter 6.3).

6.2.2 Components of the Lie

To further understand the conditions of the lie, I will explore what motivates the lie, the effect of the lie on the grieving child, and my therapeutic approach to deconstructing the lie. Children feel discomfort as they notice the discrepancy between what they are told and what appears to be true. The application of dramatherapy can reverse the harmful effects of lying: "Thus, the playspace, like theatre, is a lie that seeks to reveal itself as a lie, and therefore, is honest" (Johnson, 2009). I will break down the lie into four corollary components, followed by Johnson's (2013) four elements of the playspace.

1. ***The training of the lie.*** There is grooming and teaching the child to believe the lie.
2. ***Confusion.*** What the child thinks, they are told is untrue. If they know an object is round, yet are told it is square, shapes become confusing, and they are no longer able to distinguish one shape from the other.

3. **Misconceptions.** The child's developmentally normative propensity toward magical thinking makes them susceptible to creating misconceptions and constructing reasoning in order to live with the lie.

4. **Mistrust.** Once the truth is revealed, the child will not trust adults to tell the truth. This is damaging on several levels: (a) When the truth is discovered, there is betrayal; (b) How can the child expect the truth in the future?; (c) The child has been taught that it's okay to lie in order to avoid an unpleasant truth.

I approach the lie in an effort to deconstruct it, thereby unsticking the lie and enabling expression of the grief. Responding to these elements of the lie, my clinical interventions address each segment of the lie through Developmental Transformations (see Chapter 3). In these four elements of the playspace, dramatherapy invites the child to imagine and create within the grieving process in their primary language of play.

6.2.3 Elements of the Playspace

1. **Reversibility.** The ability to shift between roles through play. For example, when children play and reverse roles multiple times, playing both the monster and the victim.

2. **Discrepancy.** The use of representations of reality to pretend. Any object can be played with to represent an imagined world. Toys are both real and not real in the playspace, where teddy bears can have a conversation. A pencil can be used to write and, in the next moment, become a makeshift puppet the child uses to tell a story. There is a discrepancy in that the therapist and child know this is both real and not real.

3. **Mutuality.** The very nature of play requires balanced, reciprocal interactions and shared experiences. Play is mutual, as with taking turns in a game in which players agree on the rules. Should only one person be in possession of a toy or play object, withholding it from others, it is not fun. There is no play without equality, each player giving up some control to the other, inviting a mutual experience.

4. **Safety.** To do no harm. The dramatherapist is playing with the child about injury, illness, and even death; however, in the playspace no one is injured or harmed for real. Following the child's lead, the therapist indicates it is safe to play with difficult images. With that, there is the freedom to explore feelings of grief and loss.

6.2.4 The Training of the Lie

The lie begins as the answer to a situation not easily understood. A little "white lie" is created to avoid honesty. The lie is not told with malicious intent. It contains some measure of truth, misinformation disguised as information. There actually is a difficult situation to discuss, someone is chronically or acutely sick, or an illness is life-limiting. This part is true. However, the lie is driven by the liar's perception that the facts are too complicated or the event too unfortunate to speak. Therefore, the lie is motivated by a drive to change reality in a desperate desire to control. The lie lives on the fringe of reality as a construct more easily tolerated by adults, who assume it will be better for the child. From this avoidance of reality, adults create a false reality to soothe themselves, as they are the ones struggling with the truth. For the lie to take hold, the teller must repeat the lie and solicit others to spread the lie, ultimately inculcating it by persistence and repetition – training the lie.

6.2.4.1 Dramatherapy Offers Reversibility

Throughout this book, I advocate for the power and need for storytelling: for a child to be told a story that narrates their situation, tells the truth about the circumstances, and supports them before, during, and after the death of their loved one. I write narratives and construct stories for children, expressing the truth in a repeatable and organized manner, using illustrations to support this. I often co-create these with both children and parents. These stories are carefully constructed to reveal the truth so the child can understand situations that are difficult to speak about. Because these stories are presented concretely as books, the child has the authority to read and reread them. Either by holding onto the book itself or holding the story in their awareness, the child can internalize the events when they are clearly assembled, with an organizing, sequential understanding of a disorganizing situation. If the truth is read and reread, the trained lie can be reversed. Reversibility authorizes the child as the reader; the child is both in and narrating their story. Being lied to constricts the child to play only the role prescribed by the liar. Dramatherapy removes these restrictions with truth, providing shifts in roles, movement, and possibility. The child has a new narrative, a reciprocal relationship between the child and the world around them. The child now has the authority to know and tell the truth.

6.2.5 The Lie Creates Confusion

Children are very smart, aware of their surroundings, and sensitive to their parents and caregivers. A child's awareness should never be underestimated. By presenting a false construction of the truth, the child takes the misinformation and, because they love and trust the adults around them, believes what they are told. When the lie is repeated and substantiated by others around them, what they learn is not to search for greater under-standing of what they *suspect* to be the truth but fear to ask. When the child fears the answer, they will simply not ask the question. By presenting a false reality, the parent maintains control over the unknown by sharing misinformation when confronted by the child's questions.

But children notice changes. They are aware of an increase in the number of calls made or received, text messages, emails, and an increased amount of attention paid to these. They notice the changes in routine, frequent doctor's appointments, changes in appearance, relatives arriving from out of town to stay for undefined reasons, for unknown lengths of stay. They are observant and can read the moods and emotions on their parent's faces. Just as parents hear the "alarm bell" alerting them when there is something wrong – when children are too quiet or knowing something is not right in the middle of the night – children are keenly aware of their parents, too.

6.2.5.1 They Notice More Than You Think

> I told Billy he could press the button. We stood waiting for the elevator. Billy's mother, aunt, and uncle were with us on our way to my office and then to say goodbye to his father in the ICU. His mother took me aside and, lowering her voice, told me, "Billy doesn't know anything about his father's accident. He hasn't even asked for his dad once during these last two days. He doesn't know." While we rode in the elevator, Billy talked to me and looked at the hospital ID clipped to my collar. "Is that you?" he asked, "You look different in the photo." He's right, my appearance on my ID was different, a picture only slightly larger than a postage stamp from many years ago with my hair a different length. "Your hair is a different colour now, and you have bangs," he told me, looking for an explanation. "You're very smart Billy. You're right, I've changed the colour of my hair and it's grown longer since I took that picture." "Well, you should get a new picture," he told me, "So people will know it's you." The elevator door opened, and I turned to his mother telling her she may be very surprised how aware he is and how much he knows.

Given how astute children are and how much they wish to understand the world around them, it is very confusing for them to intuitively know something is different or wrong yet be told that everything is the same. A child may come into the room and see their mother crying. They ask her what is wrong. They see tears, that her eyes are red. They see the tissue in her hand. If it looks like crying, it sounds like crying, and feels like sadness, it is. However, instead of their intuitions being validated, their mother answers, "No, I'm not crying. Dust just got in my eye and my allergies are acting up."

This confusing answer offers a non-reality, delegitimizes the child's empathic understanding, alters their worldview, and weakens the child's ability to trust themselves. The adult is literally teaching the child not to trust their own instincts. By not accurately attributing or naming what is clearly happening, the adult imposes an alternative meaning to what the child knows instinctively, creating confusion about the world and, more critically, a learned distrust of their own perception.

6.2.5.2 Dramatherapy Offers Discrepancy

After falling down the rabbit hole and landing in Wonderland, Alice attempts to make sense of the nonsensical characters she encounters (Carroll, 1865). What makes sense to Alice does not make sense to them, creating a lot of confusion not only for Alice but for everyone in Wonderland. This confusion makes it difficult to differentiate between sense and nonsense, between sanity and insanity. As the Cheshire Cat tells her, "We're all mad here."

Dramatherapy invites playing with different realities. Playing with what is both real and not real helps children and adults to tolerate confusing situations. There are always dualities of life. The ability to live a healthy and balanced life (Landy, 2007) lies in our tolerating these discrepancies.

Beginning in early 2020, the world was in the grips of a virus that was little understood, virulently changing our lives and the way we interacted. The spread of Coronavirus became a global pandemic, unprecedented and full of discrepancies. We collectively struggled to understand what was known and unknown in the world and how we lived, worked, related, and interacted with each other. We were both safe and unsafe while quarantining in our homes. When we ventured out, we took precautions we hoped would prevent the spread of illness, yet we had to believe what we could not even see. We held the discrepancy of both safe and not safe.

As a dramatherapist supporting a child's grief, I use play to facilitate the child's understanding and coping with traumatic events. In response to the confusion created by the lie, play is the answer. Playing with illness to explore death and the dying process supports children in their understanding. Accepted developmental theories are well established. Freud (1962) posited the need to sublimate libidinal impulses as creative expression and therefore find more acceptable expressions of self. Winnicott (1971/2005) provided an under-standing of play as the essential foundation in life and saw play as the work of the child. Vygotsky (1967) described play as essential to social and emotional development. These and other developmental theories widely establish that children play to learn and learn through play.

In the lie, there is no discrepancy. The explanations are given and there are no questions to be asked or answered. In response to the rigidity of the lie, I offer discrepancy through the use of play. Both what is real and what can be imagined are played with regarding the grieving experience. Children do not need an invitation or explanation in play; play is their natural mode of creativity and transformation. I offer children the opportunity to play even in grief with their understanding of death and the dying process.

6.2.5.2.1 ONE FOR DADDY

A tragic automobile accident ended their father's life when Jimmy and Meg were four and five years old. Jessica, their mother, was devastated. Her life as

she had known it was suddenly and horrifically changed in an instant and would never be the same. There was objectively no discrepancy: Don was dead, an irreversible fact. Jimmy and Meg's mother was sad. They all missed Don very much. Their lives were all radically changed in an instant. The family was on their way to the Natural History Museum when the accident occurred. The children were excited to see the enormous whale suspended from the ceiling and to eat hotdogs from a street vendor. At five years old, Jimmy was fascinated by dinosaurs: Tyrannosaurus Rex, Stegosaurus, Triceratops ... His knowledge was impressive and far surpassed mine. Meg was a sweet, easygoing child. She adored her older brother and was happy to go with the flow and enjoyed whatever Jimmy liked.

The siblings began therapy to understand and process the accident, and their ability to cope with their grief. In sessions, we played. Our play took many forms but replaying the accident that took Don's life was a consistent theme. At first, their mother didn't have the ability to speak much about the accident. Therefore the children had not processed it, nor did they have words to talk about the experience. If their mother could not find words, there was no speaking.

At that first session, I took out small toys, cars, animals, people, buildings, and houses and laid them out, arranging the toys to represent the day of the accident. Across the floor, the scene created allowed the children the opportunity to act it out and reenact it. They did this again and again. With my guidance, the dramatherapy gave them all permission to speak about that day, by igniting the play and telling the story. I showed them using the toy car and small dinosaur figures what happened that day. We created their destination, the museum, and even the hotdog stand. Quickly, the children were empowered to take the lead in directing these events and adding many details to the story from their perspectives.

The children and Jessica missed Don so much on a daily basis and had a hard time with his absence. I asked them to tell me details about Don: the coffee cup he used in the morning, his favorite t-shirt, his sports team. I asked Jessica to help keep Don's memory in the house, in their day-to-day routine as much as possible. This would be hard for her, yet helpful for the children. I asked her to take out Don's coffee mug in the mornings, the one with the funny handlebar moustache that the children gave him last Father's Day. I suggested she set a place for him at the dinner table, at the chair where he always sat, and sew the top of two of his t-shirts to place over the kid's pillows, so they could hold him tight at night.

Jessica's eyes filled with tears and she looked at me in disbelief. I explained these active memories and experiences of their father could be played with. The children could imagine him there with them in the house and this their imagination had not died along with Don. It was important to create opportunities to play with him, and help the children continue remembering. As time passed the children stopped coming to see me, but several weeks before Don's first birthday since he died, Jessica called to ask me what to do. I told her we could celebrate. On Don's birthday that year, they all came to see me, and we had a party. In life Don had a moustache, and I made moustaches for us all to wear that we held on sticks and could bring to our faces. We had cupcakes: one for each of us, and one for their dad. We all wore hats, drank lemonade, tooted horns, and had fun trying to eat cupcakes with our silly moustaches. I cut Don's cupcake into two pieces and the children ate it for him. This first year and the many that have followed are hard for them, but Jessica told me that I had taught her how to keep his memory very much alive in playful and silly ways. This she said made all the difference for her, Jimmy, and Meg, giving them ways both to live on without Don and yet still with him. They were able to grieve Don in active and playful ways, to play with the discrepancies that were both real and not real.

6.2.6 The Lie Creates Misconceptions

Magical thinking is a developmental process of linking internal thoughts and situations. Magical thinking is normal in childhood and even in adulthood. For example, many adults subscribe to superstitions. Other common misconceptions about health are practiced however ill-conceived, such as you will catch a cold if you go to sleep with your hair wet. This notion gets passed down from parents to children, forming a belief that changes our practice. In childhood, many children believe their beloved teddy bear can protect them from monsters, or if they get out on the "right" side of the bed they will have a good day. There is no plausible relationship between these things, but the thought or hope that there is a connection can be a way of protecting oneself from perceived harm. In childhood, it is natural for children to see that everything that happens is related to their egocentric way of thinking, that their actions can directly influence the world around them. A child's misconceptions can become false beliefs that are not fully explored by either the teller or the recipient of the lie. The lie contributes to and supports magical thinking, linking thoughts with misconceptions.

Through play, children discover, investigate, and explore. They ask questions, formulating ideas, testing, and refining their thoughts. Children use their bodies, senses, and minds while exploring their environment, gathering information actively through their interactions with others. As children play, they retest and modify their theories, adapting in their understanding and furthering their thinking to take greater risks and have novel experiences. When a secret lurks, creativity and play are diminished. The lie becomes embedded and fixed. In order to be in a relationship with the parents, the child agrees, complying with the lie, thereby changing the child's reality and their ability to have faith in their own belief. This, I believe, is the most dangerous effect of the lie. The child learns not to trust themselves, others, or their world. Exploration, play, and discovery are diminished, leading to disorientation and confusion. If the child senses something is wrong, yet are told nothing, or told they are wrong, they learn not to ask.

6.2.6.1 Dramatherapy Offers Mutuality

Dramatherapy allows me to play and engage the child in variations, imagination, and exploration. In play, the child and I can enter alternative realities. In the practice of Developmental Transformations (Johnson, 2009, 2013), the therapist does not tell the client what to believe; there is mutual engagement in the truth and in variations of what is imagined to be true. As Johnson (2013) wrote, "The playspace, like theatre, is a lie that seeks to reveal itself as a lie, and therefore, is honest" (p. 43). The players engage in alternatives to the truth that are not lies but become playable expressions of what could be true. I offer the child a shared experience and an openness to explore their ideas.

6.2.6.1.1 THANK YOU, NO THANK YOU

I met with Gloria during several of her hospital stays before she died. Gloria had pancreatic cancer. She had lived far longer than originally expected, which was perhaps a testament to her very strong desire to live for her three little boys. But her death from cancer was an inevitability; it was only a matter of time. She was very thin. Since cancer had spread to her stomach, liver, and spine, she could no longer tolerate solid food and received nutrition through a tube in her nose.

Gloria was a gentle and soft-spoken woman. She came from a family of strong, loving women. When I would go to her hospital room, they would all be there, her two sisters, her mother, and even her grandmother. Gloria's husband often stood outside the room, looking devastated. I would ask about the children and offer my support. Gloria would thank me for coming and tell me she appreciated the offer to help, however, she would inform me the children were doing alright and she was not yet ready to tell them anything about her illness. She explained to me that she was going to get better and therefore she did not want to worry them, given she would soon be home and there would then be no need to upset them. I would hold her hands and let her know that was fine. I would tell her how much I hoped she would feel better soon and could go home to take care of her family.

I remember her grandmother, while she did not speak English, would hug me, thank me for coming, and give me G-d's blessing. As I left those visits, some of her family would follow me out and ask me to please come back, telling me they worried about the boys and knew in time they would need help to speak with them. The boys had not seen their mother in weeks and this, as well as the cancer progressing, worried the family. "How will we tell the children?" they would ask, and I gave them my card.

I ask myself: what is the difference between lying, faith, denial, and avoidance? All were present to some degree in Gloria's story. Gloria's family joined her in her desire to get better and go home, yet they also knew the truth. We found mutuality in my own hope that she would get better too, even though I knew that she could not. These two facts existed simultaneously. There was faith, hope, and desire that Gloria would get better. There was a need to avoid this truth for a little while longer. This was the way that Gloria could still care for her children, in holding the faith and hope, simultaneously withholding the truth. She could not drive them to school and baseball practices. She could not cook dinner for them or tuck them into bed each night. But for a few weeks, she would cling to hope and imagine she would once again be able to. I could still imagine it too – imagine her cooking with the children, playing, driving them to school, and reading them bedtime stories.

Before she died, I met the boys and helped their father explain her illness, the changes that they witnessed, and the progression of cancer that would end her life. During our work, we talked about all the things their mommy did with them that made her so special. We told stories about how much they all wished, hoped, and prayed she could go home.

I have deep empathy and understanding for Gloria and her holding both an objective understanding of her prognosis, as her desire to care for her children, providing and mothering them every day she could until she could not. I meet families where they are and join them during the process. With Gloria, I sensed she knew what she was asking me to do, to give her time and fend off an inevitable outcome. I played with this too, mutually enacting her need to avoid it. I understood why she wanted to wait, why she turned me away, asking me to come back another day when she was ready. In her own way, she held two truths: her faith and desire to be well, and her understanding she could not be. We played with this discrepancy. I joined her and we mutually held both sides.

6.2.7 Lying Creates Mistrust

When children cannot trust the answers they are receiving, they will inevitably stop asking questions. Their world becomes a place in which lying becomes a natural and accepted condition. Their faith in their own judgement and trust decreases. Without a world where children can trust adults to tell the truth, risk, and harm increase. The child's world becomes a dangerous and mistrusting place. The lie purports to control what is uncontrollable, and the holder of the lie is ultimately in power. The lie diminishes the capacity of those who are lied to. Lying is motivated by the person in control, who acts out of a desperate need to make sense of unfortunate events and to change reality. Facts and truth stand in the way of this control. By lying, facts are erased and there is power to be gained by suppressing. A serious divide is created between the child and the adults around them: a divide that widens as long as the lie remains, separating those who know and those who are left unaware. In a sense, two separate constructs of worldview are created and maintained.

6.2.7.1 Dramatherapy Creates Safety

The conditions of play create a safer container for exploring unspeakable things. Although absolute safety can never be fully promised, the "safe enough" principle guides the dramatherapist's use of play as a therapeutic agent of healing. In my work I wish to establish for the child that it is okay to broach challenging and difficult conversations. I communicate this within the world of play, where concepts of "real" and "not real" are explored. Children know the difference between play and reality. They know when we are pretending or not. There are discrepancies in the pretend that make it safer to explore and imagine. No real harm is inflicted, although we are free to play with representations of harm. I can play that I am hurt, fall to the ground, crying in pain, and die. However, this is not real and the child knows it. They can sense the playful tone in my voice as I play the scene. The child can in turn pretend they are hurt, fall, and die. This can be silly, and yet symbolic of something real, but not. Safety is created: the child trusts that I am not harmful, and that harmful themes can be explored safely. Dramatherapy supports the child's understanding that life does not guarantee safety, but that adults can be trusted to keep children safe. Playing instils confidence that realities can be co-created. The reasoning is restored, information is reshaped, and truth becomes a shared experience rather than a lie constructed from a place of power.

This all comes from an understanding of the source of the conditions of the lie: training, confusion, misconception, and mistrust. Lies are a defensive structure to keep the truth away. These components are inculcated to maintain a new construct: the lie masquerading as the truth. The lie, like Alice in Wonderland, continues falling down the rabbit hole, and is transported into a strange and surreal state. The deeper the lie falls, the more twisted and darker the rabbit hole becomes and the more troubling the lie is to unpack. Using the dramatherapy elements of mutuality, reversibility, discrepancy, and safety provides a way to unpack the lie and bring back truth through play.

6.3 Constructing Child-accessible Narratives

In a child's world, the healing power of a kiss and a bandage is all that is needed to know about fixing a scrape or cut. Cancer, heart attack, stroke, limb amputation, chronic illness – these are all complicated for children to understand. Medical situations are complex even for adults to understand, complicated further by the stress inherent to any hospitalization. Between procedures and treatment protocols, it becomes even more difficult. When there are young children, the strain of communicating it all is more complicated still.

For most people who are healthy, their healthy body is a privilege and a part of their identity. Our abilities and disabilities are all part of an integrated understanding of who we are. In the moments before the doctor utters the words that will change the way our bodies are known to us, the mind pushes aside the fears of the unknown. Then we are told: tumour, blood clot, traumatic brain injury. Hearing the diagnosis, the mind searches for meaning.

A common credo among therapists is to "meet people where they are at" in their process. When I meet many parents, they are in a place of their own reconciliation and swirling confusion. First, they are managing how the information impacts themselves – then considering how to speak, when to speak, and what words to say to the children.

As years passed, I found myself relying on some of the same metaphors. I found I used similar analogies and imagery to explain vastly different diagnoses: that everything in nature grows and changes; that surprises can sometimes be exciting, sometimes alarming; and that we can feel the spirit of someone's unique love for us even when their body no longer works. I repeated these themes again and again. Regardless of what part of the body, what type of illness, condition, or injury, I was using some of the same roads to get to different outcomes. Over the years, I rehearsed a way of communicating complicated concepts easily to children. I had been repeating thousands of stories about medical situations that taught me what to emphasize, and how to help children understand very complicated things. I noticed similar ways that children responded: common themes of what was confusing to many, and refined my explanations further to help them understand. When talking to children, I often break down the word spirit, as a concept the child may understand best. "Some people call it spirit," I tell them. "The spirit is also called soul or energy. But it means the Mommyness of Mommy. The special way that she speaks, the nickname that only she calls you. The favourite foods she makes and her love for you."

The first story that I wrote explaining a difficult situation was a simple black-and-white colouring book, hand-drawn by my supervisor at the time, Erika Leeuwenburg. I have written hundreds of stories for children, each individually tailored to the child who it is made for. *A Story for Joey, Mary, Sam, Sarah, Taylor, Jackson* ... the list goes on and on. The images are unique to each – not one book for every child, as most are written, but one book for one specific child. As I am not an illustrator, I use clip art and available art based on Internet searches. More recently, I collaborated with a graphic designer to realize the product more fully. This is an area I wish to continue to explore and expand further.

Each child's story includes the specific names of family members, toys, and activities they enjoy. I search for pictures from stock photos, matching the child's hair colour, number of siblings, pets, etc. The images are immediately recognizable, the child knows instantly it is their story and being able to identify, they feel seen.

The "aha" moment about telling specific stories for children came when I met a man and his wife in an outpatient infusion room. The husband had a brain tumour. They had a nine-year-old son who knew that his father was sick, but not much else. His father's treatment would take place over several weeks and was complex. The parents asked if I could recommend a book on the subject for their son. The wife told me that she worked as a librarian and had done some research to find books but had not really found anything for a boy whose father had a brain tumour. I offered to write it for him with their collaboration, asking some detailed questions about their family. After the child received and treasured his book, the value of putting an individualized story onto paper became clear: it could be written exactly to the child's reading level, following a specific illness trajectory and treatment.

I have written many stories about many different situations over the past 18 years. But each has a similarity: the explanation of complicated, difficult circumstances in the child's voice. This involves the use of developmentally appropriate, simple, and concrete language, incorporating specific vocabulary of the families. Using specific names that children call important family members helps construct an individualized story to which the child can relate. Children enjoy the details familiar to them. Even very young children can identify with the pictures used, so the images tell the narrative as much as the words.

With a beginning, middle, and an end, the story organizes the confusing, overwhelming circumstances and helps the child to understand what's going on. Understanding decreases anxiety about what is happening. The stories become their own. Children go back to the story again and again, sometimes every day to read and reread. There is a power in the ability for the child to go to a location, pick up their book in their hands, and read it, helping them cope with the situation while increasing the child's emotional literacy. You can access examples of stories and further resources on the "Store" tab of my website: https://nowhitelies.com/store or www.routledge.com/9780367461041 under "Support Material."

6.4 Developing Emotional Literacy and Speaking About Death

Piaget (1952) believed that sensori-motor development precedes cognitive learning and that children interpret the world through *schemas*. Schemas are the basic building blocks that incrementally form a more sophisticated mental representation of the world and make sense of our environment. Piaget defined a schema as "a cohesive, repeatable action sequence possessing component actions that are tightly interconnected and governed by a core meaning" (p. 7).

The books that I create with children tell a story of their experiences. More than just providing an objective book, concretizing a child's story increases their subjective understanding, helping them to express their emotions. The images and words become so familiar the child gains mastery, knowing how the story goes. They feel seen, the words tell the truth, and it is a relief that they are not alone. The child can trust that their story is told and identify with it, because it is *theirs*. Having learned to know what will happen on each page, they are not shocked by events, but are able to anticipate the ending. How the story ends is comforting; even if the situation is very sad, there is comfort in the clarity. The truth can be told in a way that is bearable and even beautiful.

To personalize the books, sometimes I include family photos of events and celebrations to remember their loved one in a special way.

There is greater anxiety when information is limited. The more mystery, the more alone the child feels and greater the confusion becomes. Children who do not understand the situation often develop behavioural changes which are a manifestation of their anxiety. Children can act out in various ways as they attempt to figure out what is going on. They report tummy aches or headaches or wonder if they are sick in other ways. They have disrupted sleep, waking up in the night to find comfort in their parents' bedroom, or delaying bedtime routines to spend more time with their parents. Often viewed as faking or attempting to get attention, these are actually sophisticated forms of expression. These changes in behaviour can be interpreted and addressed.

The story I write for the child offers explanations and concrete understanding. It clarifies the changes in the family and supports the child to increase their ability to regulate their emotions as they develop mastery over their situation.

As we become more aware and increase our understanding, our anxiety decreases. I made a short animated video to explain the relationship between information and anxiety (https://www.youtube.com/watch?v=sv_6vs5wVv0). It begins with a family soundly sleeping, when they hear strange noises that wake them up and cause concern. The father in the scene goes to investigate and we watch his fear and imagination overtake him. Looking for the source of the noise, approaching the basement door, he hears the sound getting louder and he wonders what it could be: Monsters? Snakes? Spiders? He worries about the unknown (see Figure 6.1). He bravely reaches out to turn the light on to discover a small kitten meowing. There is relief in the understanding, and fear is diminished.

Children are sensitive and aware of their parent's emotions and when the emotional tone in the home shifts during stressful times. They notice changes in posture and body language, as much as they notice the hushed sound of voices and changes in their parents' expressions. Emotional stress is felt in the body and manifests in the body. Children need a vocabulary to properly label and understand their corporal noticing. A child learns about the events occurring in their homes or in the community from the adults around them.

Lev Vygotsky's (1967) theories and research on social-emotional learning and language development are a major contribution to developmental psychology. He posited that a child can learn with the help of a more knowledgeable person who has a better understanding of a particular concept. That person, the *more knowledgeable other* (MKO), communicates intellectual concepts the child can internalize. The *zone of proximal development* (ZPD) describes a child's ability to understand new concepts and master new tasks just beyond the child's current ability – the gap between a child's existing development and what can be achieved. His concept of learning was inherently relational, involving both the child and the other.

Figure 6.1 A child's fear of the unknown from *Everything Changes* (Omens, 2017).

Vygotsky believed language plays a powerful role in the development of thoughts. Having the words to use brings relief. This is reflected in the video of the kitten: as the noise increases so does confusion, and with confusion comes anxiety. When the light is turned on, truth is brought into the light. This reverses the confusion created in the unknown and empowers the child with knowledge.

In the pages of the books I make, even very young children can follow along with the pictures, and gain understanding. The simple explanations help children understand not only the details of the unexpected events but also the feelings associated with them (see Figure 6.2). The narratives follow Vygotsky's theory of the more knowledgeable other (MKO) communicating complex information.

The personalization of the story helps the child focus, draws them in, and creates opportunities for projective identification. The children I have worked with become emotionally connected with the narrative as it is written personally for them. They pay close attention and are able to interact and express their feelings about the situation.

The story becomes the MKO. It helps the child with ideas just outside their grasp in understanding, but which they are able to master when taught. They now have ownership over the situation; they are a part of the family, not standing on the outside unable to be included. Death is not something parents

Figure 6.2 Developmentally appropriate representation of grief from *About The Baby* (Omens, 2017).

expect to explain to their children. A pet who died, perhaps – but never have they considered how to explain their own terminal illness or that of another. Through the narrative, I offer the language needed to the parents, who in turn now have the knowledge to speak about death. The power and authority are placed back into the parents' hands and, however untenable the situation, emotions can then be fully expressed.

6.5 Keeping the Faith

I do not consider myself a person who has religious faith; however, I know that I am Jewish going back several generations. My great-great-grandparents emigrated from Minsk, changing their surname from O'Minsky to Omens upon their arrival in the United States. During my parents' divorce, the Jewish traditions dissolved along with the marriage. After their separation in California during the early 1970s, my parents were each on their own searches of self discovery and enlightenment; the bong was lit with greater frequency than Shabbos candles. My grandfather was a conservative Jew, and I confided in him worried that I was not a "good Jew." Reassuringly, he said that all I needed to be a good Jew was a Jewish heart. Even today, that guides me in my Jewish identity.

My parents' relationship with religion was complicated. My mother broke from all convention to live on a commune in pursuit of enlightenment with a group of devotees following a more unconventional spiritual path. My father tried on religions like fashions: EST, Transcendental Meditation, and joined a church for Jews for Jesus. However, both my brothers had bar mitzvahs within a Hasidic congregation. I am not sure where faith landed during all this confusion. Perhaps all this vacillation between beliefs led me to this: I have never thought of myself as a person of faith.

My daughter teaches me, in her belief, that "G-d is as you know it." Although throughout my life I have known and believed in something outside of myself, I would not call it divinity, nor would I say fate or Karma. I do believe in my responsibility to control my own responses to situations I cannot control. I believe in the strength to endure, creativity, spontaneity, human connection, supporting others, love, and creating greater intimacy. I believe in magic, laughter, autumn leaves, cherry blossoms blooming in spring, and love. I do not call this destiny. Rather, as trauma teaches us, the world is random, turbulent, and chaotic; I try not to control the turbulence and chaos, merely practice greater tolerance of it. That said, however you know this experience – as trust, faith, hope, beliefs – it is an important factor in managing the stressors of daily life.

Many families I have worked with pray for miracles and believe in the power of G-d answering their prayers. They have hope and faith. They worry that telling the truth to their children will destroy faith and crush hopes, the granting of wishes dashed. Quite the opposite: my intention is increasing hope by defining what is wished for and believing in the power of love.

6.5.1 Faith in Wishes

Since childhood, I have loved a poem entitled "I Keep Three Wishes Ready" (Wynne, 1932) and held onto the belief these words taught me. The poem describes the importance of keeping wishes ready – just in case one encounters a fairy walking down the street. As the poem instructed, I kept wishes in mind and looked for fairies, always waiting and prepared for a fairy to grant them. The poem was read to me as a child, and I read it to my daughter Emma. It hangs framed in my office and many children have heard me read it to them.

On Emma's bed beside Muffin Man, a very beloved teddy bear, was her Tooth Fairy pillow. This pillow had a small pocket to place a tooth in after it fell out, to be replaced while she slept with a gift from the Tooth Fairy. This magical childhood ritual included a trail of glitter from the windowsill leading to her pillow. One night the Tooth Fairy forgot to perform her duty, resulting in an onslaught of tears and disappointment the next morning. My daughter's dismay appeared more about her disenchantment with the Tooth Fairy and dissolution of believing. Inconsolably sobbing she asked, "Is the Tooth Fairy real?" I helped her to hang onto that faith as long as possible.

Telling the truth is not the disillusionment or destruction of hope, nor am I advocating forcing the truth in a mean or harsh way. Naming what is happening in a language that the child understands is always developmentally appropriate. Supporting understanding through play separates fact from misconception and creates an opportunity for the child and family to express hope, faith, and beliefs. Caregivers fear that perhaps my words will harm the child, that the information spoken will be cruel. Additionally, there can be concern that telling the truth will manifest a bad outcome. This magical thinking projects fear onto the truth and further supports lying. Often the concern is that I will frighten or unsettle the child by telling them too much of the truth.

Supporting the child by including truthful information has the opposite effect. Truth-telling expands the possibility to co-create rituals that maintain hope, by identifying what a child wishes. There is comfort found in the repetition of these words, as there is in rituals in general: something that can connect one with self and community, restoring love and a sense of belonging. Just like the magic of glitter left behind by the Tooth Fairy as she flies, and as the *Three Wishes* poem encourages keeping three wishes ready, children can use wishes, faith, hope, and prayer that their loved ones will get better and come home. I wish for this too. Unfortunately, sometimes exactly what we are wishing for does not come true. But keeping three wishes ready, for fairies fly away, lets us to hang onto the other two wishes to use another day.

6.5.2 Marielle Taught Me about Faith

Marielle was 11 years old when her father was hit by a drunk driver on his way home from work. He was killed instantly, the officer who came to their door told her mother. Marielle had stayed late at school and when she got home her aunt was there, her mother having left with the officers who had come to notify her.

I met Marielle later that night to help her mother explain the accident to her. In a small windowless room where we spoke, Marielle taught me a deeper understanding and meaning of the power of faith. I explained to her that there had been an accident, that her dad had not suffered or been in any pain. I told her that the driver of the oncoming car had been drinking and his car drifted into the wrong lane. Devastated, unable to fully take in the information, she cried while her mother held her tight and they sobbed together. "What about the other driver?" She asked. The other driver wasn't badly injured but I didn't know anything else about him. "Did they arrest him? Will he go to jail?" Marielle was angry and wanted answers. I explained these were questions I couldn't answer. I did not know anything about those things.

"I'm here to talk to you, to help your mom explain what happened. I can only tell you the truth about what I know. That part about the other driver is not anything we are a part of, that's for the police to deal with. I'm here for you, and this is my job, to help you."

Marielle remained fixated on the other driver, insisting that he should pay for killing her father, demanding that he should be in jail and be punished. I took a deep breath and tried redirecting her. Her mother stroked her hair and looked at me desperate for the answer. *"Marielle, this was nothing anyone could control. This was an accident."* She vehemently challenged that, telling me that it was the driver's fault that her father was dead. That he shouldn't drive drunk. *"That's true, the driver was drunk, and it is illegal, but a judge will have to decide that part, I imagine,"* I tried explaining to her. Still, she continued to focus on fault, blame, and punishment.

"Marielle, sometimes bad things happen that we wouldn't have wanted, but we can't change them. I wish we could change it and that the accident never happened, but it did. I know that your mom wishes the accident could have been avoided. And your dad never wanted to be in an accident. That driver didn't wake up this morning wanting to kill your dad. He made a mistake and I'm sure he is very upset right now and is deeply sorry and wishes this didn't happen too."

In trying to assign fault and blame, Marielle was trying to solve the problem. If someone is to blame, if there is fault, then the source of the problem can be solved, like a math problem. The brain is very good at making sense of complicated algebra and geometry problems. If only the mind can solve the problem (the drunk driver losing control of his car), then the logical mind could master the problem and could prevent the accident. The factors in this incident: if her father had stayed late at work, or if he had left early; if the driver had taken a different route home, not gone to the bar, taken a taxi home; or a traffic light had stayed red longer. If any one of these things could be changed, then her father might still be alive. I explained this to her. She became angry at G-d asking, why would G-d do this?

Thoughts raced through my head: How can I speak about G-d? I'm a dramatherapist, a psychotherapist, not a spiritual counsellor … But in answering questions about G-d I am following her understanding, supporting this, not trying to condemn or change her religious faith. I am a therapist. I've never met G-d, and as I understand it, G-d does not manifest in a physical body or resemble the human form. We cannot control the turbulence, chaos or unpredictabilities in life, only attempt to tolerate them. My intention on this night, in this room, is to focus on what I know and how I can help this child.

"No one wanted this to happen. Enormous power is found in faith in G-d. What I know is that you are loved deeply by your mother and family, and that you have faith in G-d and the power of G-d's love. I believe in your father's love for you and your love for him. This is all we can control, our behaviour and our actions: for us to focus on love, caring, and the feeling of sitting near

your mother with her arms around you. That is what we can control and believe in. There is only love here in the room. What we all want is for this not to be true. What is within our control is to love and comfort each other, to hold tight onto the feeling of a father's love for his family, and to keep the faith in the power to choose love in support of tolerating the intolerable."

So I keep three wishes ready, lest I should chance to meet, any day, a fairy coming down the street.

Chapter 7

Stories in Loving Memory

7.1 Brief Introduction to Case Examples

Each child and family has their own particular cultural traits. Culture can be identified in families by religion, language spoken, and country of origin but it can also be seen in the characteristics and social norms within a family structure, even within the body itself. "Bodies of Culture" is a term created by Menakem (2017) to describe how our bodies become bearers of the history of cultural context from the moment we are born, carrying a form of knowledge that is different from our cognitive brains. The case examples which follow here include families from many different cultural contexts. What unifies them is how we worked with play to understand what might be going on in the body. I am invited and find ways to play within a family's culture, offering guidance and making a difference in a lasting way during very painful moments.

I have been rewarded with longstanding and meaningful relationships with families. Some I worked with only briefly, meeting them once or twice, other families over several weeks, months, or even years, as the illness process and treatment options changed over time. Together with each family, I joined them in watching and witnessing the changes, exploring the expectations, hopes, and anticipated outcomes.

In this chapter, I include a wide range of examples which reflect the experiences of parents, caregivers, and children. Woven throughout this chapter are reflections and letters from parents about the efficacy of dramatherapy interventions with their children and the impacts on themselves after many years. Each articulates a different personal relationship with the processes that are the core themes of this book.

7.2 Anticipatory Grief: We're Not in Kansas Anymore

In *The Wizard of Oz* (1939), the use of color is carefully applied: astonishing red ruby slippers and sky-blue gingham against Dorothy's puffy white sleeves, like clouds in the sky she falls from. The magical transformation from Kansas to the "merry ol' land of Oz" is dazzling. Watching the stark contrast of sepia tones to

DOI: 10.4324/9781003026938-7

Technicolor in one single shot draws the viewer into another world. Through colour, the film paints vivid differences in each of the lands Dorothy and her friends travel to. They do not wander haphazardly from Munchkin Land through the countryside to Oz; they are guided, told to follow the yellow-brick road. Dorothy is led there slowly, brick by yellow brick.

The road anticipating illness leading to death is complicated, and I do my best to guide families into this unknown territory. When anticipating the death of a child, siblings are often overlooked. Finding bad outcomes intolerable to accept, parents keep the illness trajectory from the child for as long as possible. Later they are forced to ask the question, "How do I tell my child?" In paediatrics, doctors will use every possible treatment and work incredibly hard to stop illness and death. In many cases, they are successful. But in acute paediatric care areas, there are inevitabilities. There are times when a child has a medical condition for which there is no cure – no medicine or treatment options, even far-reaching hope or experimental options. Death becomes a foregone conclusion. Palliative care is provided for pain relief and symptom management. Emily's story is an example of this. The deterioration of her illness was not immediate, but a gradual decline anticipating her ultimate death.

7.2.1 The Unholding of Emily

Most children with Emily's medical condition are not expected to live beyond three years of age. However, due to the amazing love and care of her parents and brother John, Emily lived far longer than any of the doctors predicted, until shortly after she turned six years old.

John adored his baby sister and was her biggest fan and fiercest protector. He was three years old when she was born. Thrilled to have a baby sister, he was patient, loving, and gentle with her. Her parents noticed that compared to John at six months of age, Emily's development seemed slower. As weeks passed they became increasingly concerned. Many doctor's visits, tests, and second and third opinions, came to an inevitable conclusion. Emily was born with a rare genetic abnormality that would end her life. There was no hiding from this as her loving parents learned about all the forthcoming changes, expectations, and how they could care for her for as long as she could live with this disease.

Her parents knew that just like they had been educated by the medical specialist, John needed to be prepared. They expressed concerns that we might scare him or that he would become scared of his sister. They worried that all the information would be too much and overwhelming for John, and wondered how we would explain to a four-year-old an illness they struggled to make sense of. I explained that I would never recommend telling a child too much information before they needed to know it. This is a common concern of caregivers, that I will "hit them over the head" with information. My practice of truth-telling is on a need to know basis. My intentions were to focus on what was different about Emily, and that differences make us all special. Specifically, how he could observe the uniqueness of his sister in order to understand and discover new ways to play with her. I explained there was no need to talk to John about things beyond today, beyond the doctor's and family's concerns, and attending to her needs in the present day. "We will work together. You will keep me informed of the changes and information you receive from the doctors, and I will help translate this into a language John can understand through play, the learning style most suited for him." I laid this out for them and began meeting with John during different phases of his sister's illness trajectory.

Emily's mother shared her reflections about my work with the family, the caring of, holding, and the unholding of Emily.

One of the first medical procedures our daughter had was having a feeding tube placed. My husband and I had a lot of anxiety both about the procedure and the realization that she would now need to be fed via a feeding tube, yet we didn't want to project our worries onto our son. Just prior to her surgery, John and Stephanie took a simple, canvas doll, and gave her a feeding tube, complete with a syringe with which they could squirt water into the doll. Not only did this help him understand the medical procedure in a very uncomplicated, and almost fun way, but it also made him feel much more comfortable with this new way of feeding his sister – one that he very often liked to help with.

When Emily got a little older, there was a period of time when John was very upset. He noticed that people often stared at his sister and that some would make thoughtless comments. John, being his sister's incredible protector, expressed his anger to Stephanie. She encouraged and helped him to compose an amazing piece of poetry, written in his sister's voice. It not only expressed how individuals' insensitive acts were incredibly hurtful to her, it also compelled others to consider her feelings and realize that Emily was beautiful and unique. Having his work displayed amongst the artwork of many other talented children, most of whom could relate to his piece, really empowered him and made him feel as though the voices of he and his sister were heard and understood.

It was 2:00 am. The physician on duty in the PICU called to tell me that Emily was actively dying, and her mother had asked if I could come in. The PICU is very quiet in the middle of the night. I entered her room and saw Emily lying in her mother's lap. The bed was raised, Emily's head on her mother's chest, Judy's arms wrapped around her daughter. Her husband, Robert was sitting in a chair close to them comforting both his daughter and wife. During these last hours of her life, the family stayed in these same positions. Doctors, nurses, and other support staff who had worked with Judy and her husband during these past four years came and went from the room, checking in, at times sitting with them, and also giving them space and time alone. Judy did not move that morning, cocooning her daughter, her body containing Emily's as her womb once had. Several hours passed and Emily died in her mother's arms, ending her life as it had begun: in her mother's loving embrace.

Stephanie, along with one of Emily's doctors and counsellors, quickly arrived in our room. After a little while, Stephanie asked if we would mind if she brought up some paper and paints. At first, I honestly wondered why she would think of painting at such a critical time. However, she suggested painting Emily's foot and making footprints – something she had done with Emily and John to make memories several times throughout the years, which the kids then gave to me for Mother's Day. After making several footprints, she then asked if I would like to paint anything else with Emily. One of my very favourite things to do was to finger paint with my daughter. Since she could not move her hands on her own, I would use her finger as a paintbrush, dip it into paint, and together we would create beautiful, colourful paintings. Although she couldn't verbalize it, it was usually evident to me that Emily enjoyed our painting sessions just as much as I did. Most of the artwork she made, we gave as gifts to friends, and I had recently been thinking that I wished I had saved more of her paintings to keep for ourselves.

I told Stephanie that I would love to make something for Emily's brothers who unfortunately weren't at the hospital with us. She quickly found some little cardboard boxes, and Emily and I began to paint one for each of them, as well as one for me, which is now one of my most treasured keepsakes. Despite the fact that she was rapidly declining, Emily seemed very comfortable sitting in my lap with her hand in mine, creating her last beautiful pieces of art.

I can honestly say that this creative arts experience brought me such an incredible amount of peace and comfort during the most devastating and heartbreaking experience of my life. Never would I have thought of creating art as a narrative keepsake with my daughter during her last few hours, but Stephanie gave both Emily and I the most wonderful gift by suggesting the idea and enabled us to share for the last time one of our most favourite activities.

After Emily died, Judy stayed holding her daughter. She stayed like that, just holding her, until early evening. Judy had not moved from the same spot since

I arrived. She had not eaten, drank much, or gotten up even to stretch in all that time, as if there was nothing she needed other than to hold Emily for as long as she could until she could not hold her anymore. When the funeral director came and it was time to make the next transition, I watched as Robert slipped his arms under and gently picked her up, bringing her into his chest and holding her against his body. Slowly he let go and passed her on, to see her next at the funeral.

The next day Judy called. They had told John that Emily died and asked me to meet with John and explain the funeral. He had a lot of questions about the last hours of his sister's life, and about the casket and the graveside, which I answered. John had some ideas about what he wanted to say at her funeral and we planned this. He wrote a story about Emily he wanted to tell. When Judy and Robert joined us at the end of the session, we talked a bit more. For John his sister's death was not a shock to him; he'd known bit by bit about her illness throughout the process. He understood how the body works and the complications incrementally affecting her as the illness progressed. He knew about the first surgery placing the feeding tube and why she needed it because she could not chew or swallow. He helped suction her mouth. Both brother and sister moved on different paths towards each of their divergent futures. So when Emily died, the news did not surprise him. John did not wake suddenly, like Dorothy, in a world beautifully transformed from the one he knew the night before. Unlike Dorothy, his view of the world changed as vibrant emerald green, ruby red, and yellow brick became black and white. Instead of her abrupt awakening, for John there was a slow fade, a gradual understanding, not too fast or without knowing.

Judy asked me if I could please come to the funeral. She also asked if I would be a pallbearer. She explained that they had asked her own therapist, Emily's doctor, nurse, and a few other people who had worked so closely with them during the years to be pallbearers as well. Judy said she wanted the people who had held her family during these years anticipating, supporting, and preparing them for this day, to help them in this final moment of her death. I do not believe there is any more accurate expression of what it means to create a holding environment in the therapeutic process, facilitating and supporting change, than the honor of participating in the "unholding" of Emily as she slowly transitioned from one state of being to another. Her mother, her father, and lastly, I walked by her side, like Dorothy with her friends transitioning brick by yellow brick.

7.3 Playing With the Death of a Parent

7.3.1 Steven and Paula's Story: "That's What Mommies Do"

I remember my initial phone conversation with Paula. She was a successful lawyer, with a six-year-old son. Paula told me her cancer was incurable, that she

knew she would die from her illness. She was extremely straightforward and honest. She reached out for help on how to speak with her son and be honest with him. She did not have very long to live and wanted to make sure he was prepared. Steven, she told me, would live with her sister and brother-in-law after her death; they would become his parents. This and many details she had prepared for. She told me her sister would need help coping emotionally and help supporting Steven as her illness progressed. "I know some people cope by being in denial," she told me, "But I can't afford to be. I need to make sure Steven is okay. I need your help."

For the first appointment, she came with Steven. They sat on the floor, legs outstretched, Steven in her lap with her arms wrapped around him. We talked about what he knew, the surgery she had had, the treatments he knew about, and the side effects. Steven looked like his mother: brown eyes and hair. In his mother's lap, Steven was a little pea in the pod. He knew a lot about her illness. We talked to him about what changes he saw, associating these with cancer's effect on her body and growth in different places. We discussed where the cancer had started when he was a younger child, what he remembered from that time, and how he could see the many changes. I wrote Steven a book about his mommy's cancer to tell him more about the things he did not understand and the details he did not yet know. I was careful not to provide too much information too quickly. Over the next few months, we filled in the blanks as things evolved.

Paula wanted to die in a hospice facility, outside of the home she shared with her son. She was transferred to the facility a few weeks before she died. Paula's sister began bringing Steven weekly when his mother became unable. We played and created stories of his family while looking at photographs of trips they had taken to help him process. We took those memories and created objects with them that he could hold and hang onto. I knew these would be important to Steven and support him in his grieving. We decorated the exterior of a box with photos of him and his mother, placing inside small toys and trinkets he associated with those memories. Steven would bring it home to show his mother and keep in his room. Steven was a very smart little boy and one day, closer to the end stages of her life, I explained how cancer metastasized.

Step by step during her illness, I had been explaining to Steven what was happening, in language with images he could relate to, helping him to understand and associate the changes in his mother with the process her illness was taking. I wrote him stories, adding chapters and information to the story as needed. We read the stories together, at times Steven reading to me. The words and the images showed him the functions of the body during both wellness and illness. We used a metaphor of a garden growing and the weeds we need to remove to help the garden grow (Figure 7.1).

The pages became familiar to him. The telling of his life with his mother, page by page, added up to where we were today. I reminded him, as we read along, where cancer had begun, that it was no one's fault; that the doctors, medicine,

Figure 7.1 Metaphor for cancer metastasizing from *Cancer Changes* (Omens, 2017).

and surgeries tried to stop it, but cancer spread, like weeds in a garden. Like weeds that overtook and hurt the flowers so they could no longer grow. This, I explained to Steven, was what was happening to his mother. The cancer was now in her liver, spine, and brain. He stopped reading and looked up at me from the page and said, "Oh, I get it. The heart pumps the blood through the whole body and it carries cancer to these other parts of her body." "Yes, Steven, yes it did."

In a new chapter, I explained the hospice facility and that there were nurses there who could help mommy in the middle of the night if she needed it. We spoke about his visiting her there and talked about the games he would bring that they could play during the last days of their time together. I also asked him to choose a special teddy bear to bring to his mother, telling him that when he went home that night, mommy could cuddle the teddy and that would help her feel good, just like his teddy does for him when he hugs the bear. The last time Steven went to the hospice centre, he brought their favourite game. They played together, Steven moving the pieces on the board for his mother who was too weak to do it on her own. He told me how proud he was to help her play the game. Steven was able to keep playing with his mother and maintaining their connection. Through play, story, active participation, and creativity, he was a *part of his mother's dying process, not dislocated and kept away. Through these, he was protected and engaged, rather than removed and separated.*

What follows is a reflection from Paula's sister, Lisa.

My sister brought Steven to see Stephanie about six months prior to her death. Stephanie worked with Steven during those six months, helping him to understand his mother's cancer, and what cancer is. My sister wanted her help, explaining what that meant was happening to her body currently at the time of each session, and his feelings and emotions surrounding his mother's illness. Stephanie continued to work with Steven for about four months after his mother passed away, to help him to transition to his new life without his mother and deal with the grief he was experiencing.

The last couple of weeks of my sister's life were extremely emotional and dramatic for us. She was in hospice and I was running back and forth between visiting her and trying to take care of Steven. There was a major snowstorm going on during the last week of my sister's life. About 24 hours before my sister passed, I knew that she was going to pass and I was so scared about the unknown and to have to tell Steven myself – I really needed Stephanie's help.

I was so nervous to tell Steven on my own that his mom passed away. It was a Saturday night and I frantically called Stephanie saying "My sister died! How do I tell Steven?"

Over the phone, I told Lisa, "Remember to breathe, it's not going to be easy." I suggested that she hold Paula's hand and talk to her about Steven. That she could place the teddy bear Steven had given her beside her. "When you go home, sit down with him and explain that you were just with mommy. That her body had slowed down and was slowing down more and more." I told her to describe to Steven that she was lying comfortably in her bed and his teddy was with her, to tell him that she had held his mommy's hand and told her how much Steven loved her. I reminded her there were pages in Steven's book, showing a toy that slows down and stops working. I advised her to tell Steven, "This is what is happening now. Mommy's body will stop and she will die."

Then two days later we were back in her office again so that Stephanie could talk with Steven about his feelings and emotions on his mother passing and to help him to understand about what a funeral is so that he'd be able to go to his mom's funeral, which we thought was important for him and his grieving process.

Sitting in his uncle's lap with Lisa and me near, we talked about his mother dying. I went over the story, so he knew what happened. How there was not any medicine to make his mother better and that she died. Her heart stopped beating and she stopped breathing. She did not need her body anymore. "Steven, your love was with her when she died. Your aunt was telling her about your love, and she held your teddy that you love so much. Love is strong and doesn't stop, even when the body does." We talked about his mother's love for him and that he could feel her love now, that that is the part that stays even after the body dies.

As tears streamed down Steven's checks, he looked at us and said in earnest, "But who, who is going to be my mommy?" Sitting in sorrowful silence, his aunt reached towards him with a tissue and wiped his nose and tears. "Well, that's what mommies do," I said, "they wipe your tears and take care of you. Your mommy will always be your mommy, but your Auntie Lisa will do the things that mommies do and take care of you. Both mommy and Auntie Lisa had the same mommy. They both learned from Grandma what mommies do. So now Auntie Lisa will take care of you, just like Mommy would have if she could. She never wanted to stop being your Mommy, but she died and asked Auntie Lisa to do the most important job: take care of you. That's what mothers do."

Like Steven, I lived with my aunt one school year and summer. Growing up, there were many times when my mother could not do the job of being our mother and other "mothers" stepped in to do the mothering for my brothers and me. They performed the tasks a mother does: the making of school lunches, bedtime tucking, and wiping of tears. Ultimately, she could not take care of herself, or us. Love is the act of mothering, and although I know Paula wanted desperately to do this herself, Lisa loved him as a mother and he would grow up to be her son, and thrive in a loving home.

Due to the phone call Saturday night, the session on Friday evening during the snowstorm, all the other dramatherapy sessions, and the session the day before the funeral, Steven was able to handle the news of his mother and attend the funeral where he was really fine. Of course, he was hysterically crying over the fact that his mom was now dead – but it was not a shock to him and he had maturely understood all that had happened with his mom's body (and mind) and how to express his feelings about it all. I know firsthand the power that dramatherapy can have on the healing process of a child through a traumatic time in their life.

7.3.2 A Familiar Gesture, One Last Time

Their father was dying and his nurse in the ICU called me on behalf of his wife, who wanted to bring her girls to say goodbye. I had never met the

family before. I would be bringing the girls and their mother from the lobby up to the ICU. There really wasn't a lot of time, and I spoke with them in preparation and asked them if they wanted to go into his room. Their mother stood between her daughters with an arm around each one. As they approached him they were crying. We stood together near the bed. I asked the children what types of things did their daddy do with them, what things did he say? They told me that every night when putting them to sleep and when he left the house, he would make the sign of the cross and bless them.

Their father would recite this in Spanish: En el nombre del Padre, y del Hijo y del Espíritu Santo. Amen. *They smiled telling me this and his wife held them tight. We talked about his sudden accident and his internal injuries, and that he would die from this. I asked them if they wanted to have their father bless them and they liked that idea. I helped his wife to pick up her husband's hand and move it in the shape of the cross as she recited this twice over the children.* En el nombre del Padre, y del Hijo y del Espíritu Santo. Amen. *In the space between death and life, they were able to be with their father in a familiar way one last time.*

7.3.3 Bubbles Are Magic

Michael began noticing he was losing his balance. Then he recognized there were times while speaking that his speech was slurring. He had been training for an upcoming half-marathon and wondered if he had been overdoing it at the gym. His wife began to notice too and was concerned. After a few weeks, it seemed to be getting worse and Jenn insisted that he go to his doctor. It very quickly became apparent that Michael's fatigue was actually a fast-growing brain tumour. Jenn and Michael were expecting their second child and their son Oliver was a year old. That spring, which started full of so much promise and excitement about the new baby, had become a nightmare. CT scans, biopsies, and surgery all determined that Michael only had a short time to live; the cancer would take his life. He desperately wanted to watch the children grow, play catch with them and all the dreams he and Jenn had hoped for, but instead, the doctor suggested they get their "affairs in order." It was devastating.

His cancer progressed very fast. Soon after Halloween, Jenn called. The social worker at the oncologist's office had given her my information. She was hesitant as to what help I could offer a child not yet two years old. I explained there were several things we could do, and there was time to be together as a family. Jenn and I met in Michael's hospital room. He was weak, needed oxygen, and the medication made him tired. Despite this, we spoke and Jenn shared many stories with me about their family. Oliver loved Elmo and Mickey Mouse, and they had taken a trip at the beginning of the summer to Disneyland. There was a photo of them with Mickey Mouse in front of the Magic Castle. They all looked so happy and healthy; it was hard to believe this was the same man.

Michael told me he did not want to die, that he wanted to be with Jenn and the children. We talked together about some of the things they hoped and planned to do as a family. When Michael needed a break, Jenn spoke for him. Instinctively, she knew what he wanted to say, she held his hand and talked to him softly, Michael nodding his head in affirmation. As they spoke I made a list of the things they told me. There were times when Jenn became overwhelmed and others when Michael did. They seemed to be in sync, Michael comforting her when she needed him and Jenn reassuring him when it was too much for him. I encouraged them and pointed to milestones, like when the children would learn to ride bikes, or graduate from elementary, middle, and later high school. What did Michael want to tell them about sharing, respect, responsibility, even dating? As hard as it was to imagine them growing up and doing some of these things, I prompted them to keep going. I asked Michael to tell me specific things he imagined he would say. He told me that he would be proud of them for trying and never to be afraid to try and fail, then try again. That Oliver and his younger brother should never forget to ask for help and be nice to each other. He told Jenn that he would let the children know to always respect their mother and do what she said. There was such tenderness between them and I stood to leave, letting them have some time together.

The next time I saw Jenn it was to bring Oliver to see his daddy for the last time. Michael's need for oxygen had increased and soon he would require a ventilator. There was no expectation he would ever come off the ventilator. He wanted to hold and kiss his son before he died. Oliver was wearing pyjamas with smiling jack-o-lanterns all over. "He loves these PJs," Jenn said, "and I can't get him to wear anything else. I had to buy another pair so I could wash them." Oliver was a very sweet little boy with light, curly hair. He insisted on walking down the long hallway holding his mommy's hand. This of course took some time, and as we walked I put my hand on her shoulder. I gave Jenn a bag containing cards I made on Michael's behalf, one each telling them what he would want to say during the times in life we had discussed. On each envelope was written, "Open on … " and inside signed, "Love, your Dad."

At the nurse's station, the team watched silently as Oliver, his mother, and I walked into Michael's room. One of the nurses turned away to cry. This I knew would be very hard. As we entered and Oliver saw his dad, he reached to his mother. Jenn picked him up and positioned him on her hip away from her growing belly. Oliver became anxious and agitated. This is normal: his father did not look like himself. There were tubes and he had an oxygen mask. Michael removed the mask and spoke to Oliver. His voice was soft and hoarse, and he mouthed the words he could not say. Jenn stood near her husband and Michael reached out towards them. She knew he wanted to touch and kiss his son, and Jenn told Oliver to give his daddy a kiss. Oliver turned away, noticing a "Feel Better" helium balloon stuck in the corner of the ceiling. From my pocket, I took out a bottle of bubbles and began to blow them. Oliver turned toward the bubbles and got very excited. We were now all looking at the bubbles, smiling, cooing, and playing at popping them. I sang a little song as the bubbles floated over Michael's head. Nodding to Jenn, I blew them slowly, one at a time as she moved closer to her husband. Michael took off the mask and kissed Oliver, reaching to touch him. Oliver knelt on the bed very near his daddy's shoulder and face. I kept sending bubbles into the air as Jenn leaned in and kissed them. Magic.

7.3.4 What Are We Celebrating?

I got strange looks from the nurse's station as I walked onto the unit carrying party streamers and decorations from the dollar store. On a food tray, I brought a pizza, some ice cream cups, chocolate sprinkles, and a canister of whipped cream from the catering manager in the cafeteria. I decorated the room as the patient slept. I hung a rainbow-colored, crepe paper sphere to the top of the curtain rod surrounding the bed and strung a garland of tassels. The children would arrive soon from school to spend the afternoon with their mom, and the room looked transformed, bright, and fun. I could see the staff, respiratory therapist, clerk, and nurses peeking in to see what I was doing.

"What are you celebrating?" someone asked me. "Today. We're celebrating today." I answer. "Today we are having a pizza party with make-your-own sundaes and watching a movie." The children ate their pizza and finished the vanilla ice cream for their mom because she was not hungry. We put a movie on a laptop, each child finding a cozy spot beside their mom. She brought her arms around them both as they nestled against her.

It is the most natural thing: to cuddle with mom and watch TV, to rest in the comfort of her embrace. On this visit with their mom, they would remember the pizza, ice cream, cuddling, and their favourite movie. They would all have one more memory. Their mother could know the peace of having her children near, knowing they were happy and calm. On that day, this is what we celebrated. We never know how many celebrations are left.

Later, one of the nurses told me that they had fallen asleep like that. Her patient said she had never felt so relaxed as sleeping with the children near her.

7.4 Playing With the Death of a Sibling

7.4.1 Peek-a-Boo

The baby had a fever and his mother put him down for a nap. When she checked on Mark he was not breathing. She screamed to her husband that the baby was purple and to call 911. Andy, Mark's three-year-old brother, came into the room. Their mother was hysterical and tried to resuscitate her six-month-old son.

This is the story I was told in the PICU when I got to work. I entered the room where the baby was. He was on a respirator and Andy was at the end of the room on the floor, playing with a truck. Andy was curious about my presence in the room, as I held out toys that piqued his interest. Hesitantly, he approached me and stood behind his mother's leg, peeking out at me. I mirrored this, looking away and peeking around to find him. Our game of peek-a-boo slowly transformed with the addition of the "boo" at the end of each peek.

Sound and movement circles are familiar to most dramatherapists and actors as a warm-up intervention to establish interpersonal group cohesion. Here in this room, we were warming up to each other, finding a common language and play that Andy was comfortable with. The "boo" took on an expression as we began to "boo" a bit louder with the addition of fright upon discovering each other. Andy and I played this game on and off while I was speaking with his parents. Hearing more of the story, I interpreted the game Andy and I were playing. This was a game of discovery, fright, and shock upon finding the other.

This is what happened in the house several hours ago: Andy's mother was scared upon finding the baby unresponsive, deprived of oxygen, his body blue – or as she screamed, "purple." His parents told me they were concerned about Andy, that he did not understand what occurred. They felt he was too young to comprehend and his mother dissolved in tears, completely at a loss about how to tell him that his brother would not survive. I explain to his mother based upon his play that I believe he is trying to process what he saw and, although he lacks the language, that this actually could be explained to increase his understanding.

I wrote Andy a book, showing him pictures that tell the narrative of what he witnessed. Andy sat with me attentively while we read. When I finished, he wanted to read it again and we did, many times. The story explained how the lack of oxygen is why his brother's skin changed colour and how this affected his body. In the book, pictures with simple words show how the doctors tried to help, but that he could not recover from this and would die. The last page showed images of the toys Andy most enjoyed playing with. He shared his hope of playing with them together when Mark was bigger. Before Andy left the PICU that night, he chose a toy he most wanted to play with Mark. He got on the bed next to his brother. I doubled for Mark, saying the words I imagined he would one day have spoken to his big brother Andy. In a world of imagination, they could play together. Andy would always be Mark's big brother, even though he could not go home and play.

7.4.2 Brother Toy

When Brian called me, letting me know he had been accepted at college, it made me feel old. How could fourteen years have passed since that little boy

who loved Mickey Mouse and held my hand from the waiting room to my office? How could it be possible he was going to college? I had seen him for sessions sporadically during the years since. He had come for therapy to support coping with anxiety during times of change. This time, the reason for the call was to ask if I wanted to read his admissions essay. I fully expected the essay to be about the death of his older brother. The topic, losing his brother when they were both so very young, would certainly have set him apart from the thousands of other essays about volunteering at local community centres. What I read was not at all what I expected.

As clinicians we ask ourselves, how is dramatherapy healing? How do we measure the validity of the work? How are the elements of dramatherapy – the use of story, reenactments of situations, metaphor, spontaneity, and improvisation – effective interventions? Brian's essay was about his therapy. He reflected on our sessions, what he remembered, and how this shaped him and his future aspirations. I could not believe the gift I received reading his words. Brian described the characteristics of dramatherapy from his own perspective.

His essay that follows offers descriptive research and potential answers to these questions.

I have always loved to tell stories. As I grew and matured, I found new and exciting ways to tell them. When I was younger, toys were my method of choice. Every figure from Buzz Lightyear to Mickey Mouse was important and had its own identity. I loved mixing two worlds into one, drumming up all sorts of unlikely combinations, like Scooby-Doo and Batman, for example, seeing what kind of adventures and mischief I could get these characters into. I would lose myself in this world for hours, so deep into a story that it was hard to imagine these characters actually did not go together. I even had a partner in crime to help me, my brother Jake. My brother was born with several heart defects and had surgery as an infant. Jake was as much of an iron horse at age five as my parents are, yet one day after enduring so much not even Jake's heart was strong enough. On the day Jake died I was three, fourteen years later I can still remember it as if it were yesterday. My parents had their wounds to heal, but they put me first as they always do. My mom began taking me to a "Child Life Creative Arts Therapist," but that name was too long and I preferred her real one, Stephanie.

Although I cannot remember first meeting Stephanie, I can remember the thrill I got when I walked into her office to greet her, but more importantly, her sandbox, which was lined with toys! I am happy to have laughed, cried, learned to say what was on my mind, and to overcome what plagued it. Stephanie taught me how to allow Jake to live on in my life so that he can continue to help me tell a story. That encouragement introduced me to an entirely new creative outlet for my stories: writing. I wrote "A Story About Two Brothers" and performed it at a showcase, *marking a transition for me. I was now frequently putting my stories onto paper, a much more mature way to express myself than with my toys. This then led to my decision to write and recite a speech for my middle school's annual oratorical contest. It was nerve-racking at first but at the same time, I was excited to embark on a new storytelling endeavour. I learned not to live life afraid.*

Amidst the daunting transition into high school I had only one interest in mind: keep telling stories. I am privileged enough to tell new stories through my podcasts and interviews every day. I will never stop story-telling. I have not shied away from any topic and have no shame in telling a story that makes you cry over one that makes you laugh. I always write from the heart, one that's healthy and full of energy to race a mind that is spewing out ideas for what lies in the story ahead.

Brian had witnessed his brother's death. Dramatherapy offered him opportunities to understand, process, and cope with his grief (Omens, 2014). Brian was three years old and his brother Jake was five when he died of a cardiac event. They were best friends. Since then, his mother reported that he had become withdrawn, had trouble sleeping, and displayed regressive behavioural changes. Understandably the family was still in shock, and his mother needed guidance to help him process what happened. Our individual therapy sessions took many forms. He had very little understanding about the reason Jake died. We explored developmentally appropriate books about the working of the body and the integral function of the heart. Together we made the abstract more concrete: viewing cartoon images of the human body and the heart, drawing pictures, and using our imaginations through dramatic play. These interventions enabled Brian to contextualize what he saw and why Jake died. We had our sessions weekly for about two years.

Brian loved the sandbox and projective play. In the sandbox he told me stories and shared memories about the games he played with his brother. The themes of his play often were of loss and losing; he buried toys in the sandbox and would invent dramatic rescue scenes to find them again. He often wondered if other children that I saw for therapy also played with these same toys, expressing his concern they might be moved, lost, or taken between sessions. He would ask to hide his favourites under my desk, a pillow, or a chair, telling me he would find them again when he came back. I would promise to take care of them while he was not in the office.

We made a memory book, a scrapbook with family pictures that include photographs of the two brothers together. He drew pictures, explaining that a scribbly line was a train at the zoo, or that saturated blobs of colour represented Mom, Dad, himself, and Jake, who was always included. After many weeks creating the book, Brian took it home and kept it in his room.

As our time together progressed, he wanted to remember not only photo images of his brother, but also home movies "starring" Jake and Brian on Christmas morning, Thanksgiving and other special days. We watched these together in my office while he sat beside me and talked about Jake. He told me what he remembered from scene to scene and details about his brother. Brian had the capacity to regulate his emotion, stopping to say "This is too sad" when the content became too overwhelming and he wanted to pause and move onto something else.

"Zoom! Zoom!" went our paper airplanes, as we ran, chasing each other around the room. Brian called our sessions "playing with our imaginations." We played "blast-off," getting into our imaginary rockets, counting down, and then "blast off to heaven." When we landed, Jake would be waiting for us. In this wonderful magic world we created, Brian would talk and play again with Jake. There was reversibility in our play: I would play Jake, and then we would reverse roles and I would play Brian while he got to be Jake, telling himself all the things he wished to hear his brother say.

Sometimes we reenacted the day of Jake's death. We engaged in a mutual understanding of these events, where I could mirror back to him and share his experience. As time went on, I learned new details about the day of Jake's death as Brian taught me to play and replay this scene with him. This was both real and not real; the play represented the real event, yet was also a playful reenactment. At times, Brian would drop out of the character, come back to the "real" world of the office, and tell me details: Jake's body suddenly shook, a startled expression on his face. Brian too looked shocked by what happened as he recounted this memory. Jake fell to the ground. Jake had a sudden and unexpected cardiac event. Brian remembered in great detail that his mother was screaming and his grandmother called 911. Then the paramedics came and Brian was very scared. He told me where he hid, and I hid there with him when we got to this part of the story. I was playing myself, his therapist, but also a part of him – a part that knows he is not alone in the grief he feels and that these details, now shared, were no longer his alone.

Brian asked to come back to treatment at age 12. He had more questions about his brother's condition and wanted to know more details about the day he died. I answered honestly what I knew, and offered that for other questions we could ask the doctor. He told me about his memories of our initial sessions together playing with our imagination. He remembered me saying "It's time to find an ending," at the close of each session. This was a surprise to me. That was exactly what I said to him, and is still what I say now to clients as we end our sessions. Those words, he reflected, helped him learn that not all endings came abruptly and without warning.

Brian also told me he was afraid that he had forgotten things about Jake and how they played together. I told him that I remembered, that he could have my memories. I repeated back to him what he had told me in both words and play. We turned this into a play called "A Story About Two Brothers" that Brian was *able to perform at school. Jake was portrayed through the role of The King, his younger brother through The Rascal. The story took place on a beautiful day, when The King and The Rascal set off on an adventure. It described their escapades throughout the day: investigating a dark cave, climbing a huge mountain, and floating in a river. At the end of the day, there was a competition. The Rascal challenged the King to race. The prize to whoever wins the race was to give the loser a hug and tell him that he was a good brother.* Ready, set, go! *They raced, faster and faster, neck and neck, until ever so slightly the Rascal darted out in front of his brother and won the race!* "You know what you have to do now," *said the King. The Rascal gave the King a big hug and told him,* "I love you. You are a great brother and every time we play together we have so much fun."*

Keeping Jake's memory alive was deeply important to Brian. The play allowed him to go on with his life while keeping his big brother with him, even though he would go on to have many adventures without Jake. Through embodied expression, dramatherapy offered a concrete way to process Brian's grief.

7.5 Playing With the Loss of an Infant/Neonate

Children rehearse life, mimicking the actions of the caregivers around them: parents, teachers, first responders, and the like. Through playing, the child makes sense of and begins to integrate them into their lexicon, making meaning of the caregivers' tasks and behaviours. During our lifetime of learning and roleplaying, individuals take on and play many roles (Landy, 2007). The meaning of role, as derived from the theatre, is a distinct pattern of defining behaviours. People have the ability to imagine themselves taking on the styles of another in order to explore and better understand the role. Those around us, responding and reacting to our behaviour, provide the integration of many different roles into everyday life.

Long before a baby is born, even before conception, there is a vision of their presence. During pregnancy, new roles are envisioned: parent(s) and child. Through imagining, caregivers explore how these roles will be played once the child is born, and aesthetic balance (Landy, 2007) between the roles found and integrated. Expectant caregivers imagine their incipient child's gender, whom they will resemble, a name they will be called, and how they will embody their role. The caregivers have many hopes and dreams for the baby waiting to be born. Parents begin to take on their own new role: inside themselves, between each other, and related to the unborn child. The birth of the baby affects the roles they previously played.

While parents can conceptualize their new roles prior to the birth, the roles are merely played out in their imagination. Over time the role gradually solidifies through performance: they begin rehearsing by buying new-born clothes, filling their home with props needed to play the role. The emerging roles become further defined after the birth of the baby. The fledgling role of the parent is put into action, played more fully in relationship to the role of the child. But if the new-born dies, what then becomes of the roles of parent and child? Typically the roles are not spoken of, as if by not discussing them the parents could forget – or perhaps they are no longer thought to be parents if their baby dies. Could a parent forget their child, whether they were all together for minutes, hours, or days? How can the story of their child remain? However, the memory and meaning of that baby do not die; their role does not cease to exist after death.

7.5.1 I'm Not Going in There

It was discussed among the interdisciplinary team members that we would meet with the family in the conference room after lunch. The team consisted of the neonatologist, the baby's nurse, the social worker, and me. We all knew this room, the conference room where we had assembled many times before, with innumerable families, discussing many difficult situations. The doctor asked me if I could find the family and bring them into the room. I had established a relationship with the mother, father, and older brother, and knew them well during the weeks and months their baby was in the NICU (neo-natal ICU). On this day, the older sibling was at school and I found the baby's mother and father in their son's room. As we walked down the hall towards the conference room, suddenly the mother stopped. I felt her freeze beside me. "No," she said, strong and clear. "I'm not going in there!" she cried. It was as if as we approached the room she felt a change in the air, could feel it in the hallway approaching the room. She grasped that by entering that room, she would exit into an entirely different universe and she was scared. Her mother's intuition was correct: the truth would be told in that conference room. It was unavoidable. Despite the desire to do so, there was nowhere to hide. It was as if she was standing on a conveyor belt drawing her nearer to the words she most dreaded. She feared she could not bear it, and yet when she was told honestly her strength proved greater than she imagined. Her world was altered, but she did survive.

As any parent who has had an infant in the NICU would testify, it is a highly complicated environment. No parent imagines the first days of their baby's life anywhere but in their arms. Yet, if something goes wrong in pregnancy or the delivery room, it can very quickly turn everything the parents dreamt into a nightmare. The baby leaves the protective body of gestation, forced from the warm temperature, darkness, and languid period during which life developed, emerging into bright lights, a cacophony of sounds, and a harshly divergent environment. The medical team must be highly skilled and competent, coordinating the dance between Labour and Delivery and the NICU. This choreographed movement between unborn and born, from their mothers into the hands of the neonatologists and neonatal nurses, is well-practiced in the NICU. However, the steps and sequence are unfamiliar and shocking to parents.

The full-term infant, born between 39 to 40 weeks of gestational age, appears "normal" and "huge" in comparison to prematurely born babies. Premature babies are born as early as 24 weeks of pregnancy, some weighing under two pounds (.9 kilograms). They are admitted to the NICU. Full-term babies remain close to their mother's bedside; their sweet little cries fill the hallways of the postpartum hospital unit. The experience for those prematurely born and their families is different in every way imaginable. No flower bouquets or pastel-coloured balloons decorate the rooms. Instead, the only sounds heard are the mechanical whirr of ventilators and beeping monitors. The skin of premature babies appears translucent; there is no fat covering their tiny bones. You can hold one of their hands on the tip of your finger, like a thimble. In Labour and Delivery, all the women share a common bond: pregnancy. Each is, in the words of Plath (1971/2016, p.44), "a mountain now, among mountainy women." They are knit together, round with possibilities – yet not all are destined for the same postpartum experience. Most births follow a natural progression, but others are hurled quickly into a different world of risks and statistics.

Although it may be a family's first experience in the NICU, it is not mine. I learn from each family's story, gathering knowledge and experience to support the next parents I meet. Often I say transparently that I cannot imagine what they are going through; that I am a stranger to them, yet intimately involved in this painful experience they never anticipated when they were expecting.

How could some semblance of "normal" be preserved in this new world, with the imagined outcomes unfulfilled? Between the wished-for life of the child and the stark reality of the NICU, there is a liminal space. Neither fully in death nor fully in life, there is an opportunity for a rite of passage in this ambiguous middle place.

Together we work to create the most "normal" abnormal experience possible – to preserve memories, finding precious ways to hold meaning and permanence for a child who will never come home as expected. There was a mother who had dreamed of being pushed gently in a wheelchair through the front hospital entrance, her new-born wrapped soft and warm in her lap. She dreamed of balloons and flowers packed into the car and strapping her new-born into his car seat for the journey home. We wrote this down, the feelings and descriptions she had hoped for, and placed it into the small box holding the only items she would take home from the hospital after her baby died. We bathed and dressed her baby, wrapping him into specially purchased blankets and surrounding him with plush toys.

The scene can be staged when a baby dies, and parents can participate. They can have the experience of holding and caring for their child, even if it is for the last time. The following letters were written by mothers who lived this NICU experience. They wrote about how dramatherapy, narrative, and the power to imagine affected and continues to affect them.

7.5.2 The Story of Eleanor and Graham, as Told by Their Mother

> *The footprint moulds, the "Thumbies" necklace[1], a framed image of his hand and footprints, these objects in a box of the only belongings he ever had from the hospital. These are the only tangible things we have of him since his life was so very short. But, we knew we had to quickly pick up the pieces and hold strong for his twin sister, our daughter, Eleanor. One week later, we found ourselves in an even deeper, darker hole than before. Eleanor's fight became too hard for her little body to endure any longer. We were shattered to tiny pieces. Broken and inconsolable. Lost. [...] We needed your calm, compassionate ways, and innate ability to do all the things as I would have done them, to help us through this inconceivable time in our lives.*

Eleanor lived about a week longer than her brother. In those few days, some suggested the parents should "move on" and think of Eleanor individually. More accurately, during the days following her brother's death, Eleanor was not an only child, she became a "twinless" twin. There was no "un-twinning" just because Graham died; they would always be twins, always be remembered as their parents' first-born babies. This distinction is paramount for parents who experience the death of a twin, the death of any child. Subsequently their parents had another child, a daughter. She is the youngest child – and her older siblings are remembered as such – rather than the only child.

7.5.3 The Story of David, as Told by His Mother

> *Walking into an Intensive Care Unit is overwhelming. The bright lights come off as intrusive. The beeping noises are foreign. Being wheeled into the Neonatal Intensive Care Unit after a traumatic Emergency Cesarean Section to meet your 1.2 pound micro-preemie is unfathomable. You are being thrown into a world in which you are wholly unprepared for. The small, closet size room is overtaken by the intimidating incubator that now holds the baby you were supposed to be growing inside your body for the next 16 weeks. The body you feel has betrayed you, an empty vessel. A stark contrast to the chaos that is unfolding before you.*
>
> *I had been in the NICU as I would learn to call it, a few weeks before meeting a Child Life / Creative Arts Therapist called Stephanie. I had been spending my days in the small, dark, windowless room learning anything and everything I could about my son, David. I learned how to facilitate his daily caretaking. I tried to keep up with the medical jargon I was unaccustomed to.*

I watched every movement, every facial expression, every procedure. I was present for the Morning Rounds where the Neonatologists would outline my son's day for me as I sat in the dark corner trying to make sense of what they were saying. I was longing to feel as if I had some control as David's mother. On this particular day, I was in the dark lit room letting my son sleep when a friendly face asked if she could come in. I really was not in the mood for a new face as it had been a bad evening for David and I didn't want his sleep interrupted. Anyone who has ever stayed in a hospital knows how precious undisturbed sleep is. It is no different for even the smallest of patients. Stephanie came in, washed her hands, and asked if I wanted to make a bracelet. I was so confused. A bracelet? I wasn't even wearing my engagement ring most days in fear of scratching David by accident or the germs that I may carry in wearing jewellery. There was something about her warm smile and energy that I conceded against the inner argument within myself. It was so nice to just sit in a room with a window that let in all the sunshine. I gave Stephanie a brief overview of my background and spoke about David. I tried explaining the complicated procedures he had been receiving since his very first week. She looked at me confused and explained she wasn't well versed in the medical minutia, and she was with me to offer support. I was so used to having to explain every detail myself and it was nice not to feel the pressure. I'll admit, I felt silly making the bracelet but it was relaxing and I found myself to really enjoy my time with Stephanie. She invited me to her weekly scrapbook nights for the parents in the NICU and I gladly accepted.

Over the next few weeks, I found new confidence. David had been growing and while we still faced a mountain of challenges and surgeries, I was feeling empowered. I had someone on my side who made me feel heard. Stephanie made me feel seen. I now looked forward to the time we spent together. No matter how bad my day was, Stephanie was there to listen and didn't judge. She was there to stop in and check to see how WE were doing. David and I. Those Scrapbook nights became my favourite day of the week. It was one hour a week where I could be creative, eat a cookie, have a cup of tea, and just be. I was surrounded by other parents in the NICU and we were all facing struggles and milestones. We had a sisterhood and someone we can trust that was constant in this world of uncertainties. My family even joined a few times during our six months stay in the NICU. It truly was some of my happiest memories and the scrapbook itself is priceless.

Weeks turned into months and David was still in the hospital. We had been through seven surgeries and countless procedures. Even though David's condition had become increasingly unstable, I felt confident in the decisions I was making as David's mother. Stephanie was there for every major decision and surgery. She sat beside me in a room full of doctors and specialists and helped explain how I felt. She was there to comfort me when my husband couldn't be there. She was there to distract me from the high pressure I was feeling on a daily basis. She was there to encourage me in being the best advocate I could be for David. With her guidance, I was the person the neonatologists came to for information on David. She helped coax out the confidence to speak up when my mother's intuition nudged at me. I had found my voice even when I felt as if I was stepping on toes by doing so. I had become confident in my decision-making skills and found a new norm in the unstable NICU. I had found myself in a routine and false sense of security during the last few weeks I spent in the NICU.

The last day of David's life came as unexpected and hit us like a ton of bricks. David had survived every surgery, every sickness and yet, his fragile body had enough. We were faced with having to make the hardest decision. I was being pressured to make such a monumental decision all while consoling my husband and I asked for Stephanie to be called up to the room. The second I saw her, I took a deep breath and braced myself for what was to come. She stayed with us those last few hours of David's life. She was able to help us get my family into the room for one last visit. She stayed by my side as my son took his last breath. She had arranged for a photographer to come to take photos of my family after David's passing. During the photoshoot, I was finally able to see how effortlessly my husband could carry and hold our son. No wires, no leads, no needles. Just a father holding his baby boy. I saw how much he loved David and for that, I will always be grateful. He was our baby, our David and it felt as how it should have been. I was having a hard time letting my son go and Stephanie was the one to take him from me. There is no one else I would rather hand my son off to. I knew she would take care of him as I left the room and his physical body for the last time.

After David passed away, my husband and I struggled with the reception we would get when talking about our son. Once again, Stephanie was there to reassure us in talking about our son in the present. She assured me it was normal, healthy even. We keep his memory alive in our daily conversations and talk about what he would like. We add him to our yearly Christmas card as every other parent does. We celebrate David's birthday every year. We cut him a cake and blow out his candles. He is ever present in our lives even after death and we wouldn't have it any other way. We are so grateful to have had the support we never knew we needed in Stephanie.

At a time determined by them and no one else, the parents like those earlier needed to leave the room. To leave their babies and drive home to face the empty nurseries. To pack the clothes laying ready. To find ways to breathe and keep breathing. To walk out of the hospital with no wheelchair, balloons, flowers, or car seat. To learn to live life with only memories of their baby to hold.

At this moment, I tell families that if they are ready to leave I will stay with their baby. They hand me the baby and I hold them as the parents kiss them, hold each other, and walk out the door, parents without their baby. I tell the child in my arms that their parents love them. I know there is comfort in this for the family: that the baby and the memories are not left isolated and alone. Together with the families in this liminal space, I will not forget.

Dramatherapy provided ways for these families to play with the memory of their infant, to continue to hold their hopes and dreams for the roles of parent and child. The parents are not alone in this; I too hold the life of their child in my body and my thoughts. I have held these children while they were alive, and do so still in death.

Note

1   A necklace featuring the embossed footprints from an infant. In older children, prints can be taken of their thumb.

Chapter 8

Considerations

8.1 Challenges and Limitations of Truth Telling in Grief and Bereavement

Death is at once unequivocal and the ultimate ambiguity: a paradox. Historically, religious practice arose out of, in part, a need to explain death, life, and human suffering in order that we can inhabit the absurdity and contradictions of our being with a greater clarity and purpose.

Dramatherapists treat disorders through dialectic processes that reveal and establish states of paradox as preferred states of functioning. In drama, "Yes, and …" is a pillar of improvisation. It's the acceptance principle – when someone in a scene states something, their partner accepts it as truth. The "and" part of this principle means that a statement can be true and also allow other possibilities.

The purpose of treatment is to support people to tolerate living in these places of unknowing, of the "Yes, and," and of the profound instability of being. This is evidenced when life-limiting illness and death occurs. The insecurity between knowing and not knowing, controlling and being without control, is the ground for strong emotion and beliefs. The nature of life itself is the first barrier to truth telling in grief and bereavement with children.

8.1.1 Lack of Trained Professionals

There are numerous challenges to truth telling, not the least of which is the lack of trained professionals. In the United States, 1 in every 14 children experiences the death of a parent or sibling by the age of 18 (Judi's House/JAG Institute, 2020). The numbers show that far too many of these children do not receive the support needed to address their grief and loss. Furthermore, there are not enough trauma-informed, clinically competent grief therapists to provide support and resources.

8.1.2 Denial of Death

Parents and caregivers are often informed by their own lived experiences with grief and loss. These experiences can contribute to choices made at the crucial

DOI: 10.4324/9781003026938-8

time of the loss regarding children. Denial of death and the parents' need to address their own grief can also contribute to a minimization of the needs of the children who have experienced a loss.

When death enters a child's experience, there is a heightened concern on the part of adults to "do the right thing" and to do so with a certainty that death in all its ambiguity, pain, and mess prohibits. Well-meaning, grandparents, aunts, uncles, and neighbours share advice about what to tell the child. This is true in the hospital, too: doctors, nurses, and other health care providers often contribute opinions, regardless of whether it is the clinician's field of expertise or not. Advice about what to say to the child is often given based upon the adults' lived experience with grief and loss, not on the developmental understanding and needs of the particular child, or clinical experience and area of specialization.

The unbearable nature of the unknown contributes to challenges in inhabiting the intolerable liminality that death creates. It also inhibits the ability to seek out experts who can assist the family in finding answers. Everyone wants it all to be done, grief to be done, pain to be done. The pain of tolerating the intolerable space in between life and death creates too much anxiety. It is highly possible that parents spend more time researching the best stroller or nursery school than exploring resources for how to tell children about death.

8.1.3 Parental Consent

Another barrier to truth telling is parental consent. Many times, parents or caregivers do not give consent for appropriate skilled professionals to speak with their children due to many of the previously named factors.

If it is possible for a professional to meet with the parent in lieu of meeting with the children, it is important for the professional to explain to the family why it might be helpful for the child to receive professional support. These conversations can be an important first step in ensuring that children receive information and support that will be clarifying and direct.

But in the midst of a devastating life event, how many families are willing and able to enter into these conversations? They happen outside the procedures and interventions to the patient who is the focus of the medical care and the purpose of the hospitalization.

8.1.4 Cultural Beliefs

Cultural beliefs also may prevent families from seeking guidance from someone outside of their social network. Many families with strong religious beliefs may only accept support that relates to their faith. Some families do not subscribe to the practices of western medicine and may be wary of recommendations from others not within their communal collective. I have confronted this many times: families who respect my recommendations and thank me politely but seek guidance from within their network of shared attitudes and beliefs.

8.1.5 Funding

The grief and bereavement needs of children whose parents are in adult unit areas of the hospital fall outside typical funding sources for hospitals. Support for the child of a dying or dead parent is not billable service. The parent is the patient, not the child.

Children who are the identified patient are treated in paediatrics. Funding is allotted for the emotional needs of children who are receiving medical care and their siblings. In the adult unit areas, the emotional needs of the patient are addressed and oftentimes this includes the patient's primary caregiver. But there is limited and, more often, no funding for support services for the children of the dead or dying. Neither department, paediatrics nor adult care, is a stakeholder. Insurance is not covering the children. Coupled by the discomfort addressing these issues, there are significant gaps in services to address these needs.

During my 18 years in the hospital, I performed this particular work outside of my assigned role within paediatrics. I was known by doctors and nurses in the adult care units to address the needs of these children and was sought out as a resource. But my professional services were extended by my department with the adult units as a courtesy, not as a necessity. This work occurred in the margins of the hospital system and was not recognized within the hospital as a formal position or job.

8.1.6 Staff Training and Screening

Staff training is necessary to ensure that referrals are made when children in a family might be in need of therapeutic support. On-going in-service training when staff are brought on-board to address misconceptions and inherent bias about the needs of grieving and bereaved children would also be necessary.

Hospitals are not therapeutic communities. They are designed to address the medical needs of the patient. Working with the children of the patient will always remain secondary to the express medical needs of the patient. In a medical emergency, often the question of supporting young children is not asked. Many times staff say that they never knew there were children affected. Crisis assessments in emergency rooms should include questions about children.

8.1.7 Access

Additionally, there are challenges of access. Parents' abilities to bring a child to therapy are stymied by the emotional toll of already struggling to complete the tasks of everyday life: arrange carpools, complete meal preparation, get the children to other after school activities, and so on. Life-limiting illnesses disrupt every daily task and every daily experience for the entire family. Whether death is sudden and unexpected or progressive, it occurs at all hours of the day and weekends. Access to therapeutic support needs to be available 24/7, through a team and on an on-call basis.

8.1.8 Therapist Bias

There are consequences for not telling children the truth which can have a lifelong impact. Truth telling to children about death and dying requires the therapist to confront their own countertransference and resistance toward talking about the end of life. The interventions described are in large part offered during moments of diagnosis, crisis, and active phases during the progression of illness. This is not easy and calls upon the therapist's awareness of their own past history, not only personal but also professional. Clinical competence is gained through repetition; it is in the doing and redoing that my understanding deepens. I challenge the reader to remain open, joining me in my reflections here and wish to expand the limits of our collective understanding and support of bereaved children.

8.2 Recommendations for Future Study: Funding, Training in Palliative Care and Systemic Reforms to Facilitate Improved Communication With Children Experiencing Loss

Social change to benefit children facing grief and loss requires heightening awareness among policymakers. This should be done to support holistic family-centred care and to ensure that children receive the attention necessary to meet grief and bereavement at all levels of their development. It would take significant commitment and support on the part of hospital administration to implement the programs needed to support children outside of paediatrics. This transformation would require teamwork and dedication to elevate the importance of a child's needs as part of a larger, more holistic system of patient and family care for adults. Resources would also need to be allocated toward salaries commensurate with the advanced clinical skill needed to fulfil this role.

This process would begin with needs assessments at regional cancer, palliative, and hospice care centres treating adults both on inpatient and outpatient bases. Needs assessments would look at how many children whose parents or caregivers are receiving treatment are, themselves, receiving support through the hospital systems.

In my 18 years of doing this work, it has never been funded by hospital administration. The validity of the work speaks for itself: grieving children have needs, and the implementation of dramatherapy can meet these needs. Limitations lie rather in administration, policymaking, and funding.

The National Consensus Project for Quality Palliative Care (2018) outlined a standard for practice guidelines for family-centred palliative care in the United States. The authors included domain-specific standard practices of care for interdisciplinary teams to support the psychological and psychiatric patient- and family-centred care needs. They addressed the needs of paediatric palliative patients, including siblings. Yet there is a gap in the standard of care which disregards the specific needs of the children of dying adults.

It is my hope that this work inspires future research, determining the number of children who are severely impacted by the death of a parent. Information collected through hospital records and patients' demographics information collected of mortality rates of parents with young children.

Studies of children affected by a parent's illness could be conducted to learn, what information may have been provided, the level of understanding the child has, and the information given to the child? The perceptions of the caregivers as to what information they feel should be provided. What was the percentage of children who received therapeutic support through the hospital? At what point in the illness trajectory were they given information? The results would assess quantitatively the validity and efficacy of appropriate therapeutic support for children.

Based upon the demonstrated need for such support, hospitals would do well to create roles for primary therapists, creative arts therapists, child life specialists, and care coordinators positions. This is a specialized area of expertise, requiring advanced post graduate training. Recognition that the role demands proper training and adequate funding compensatory to the skills needed and value added by addressing grieving and bereaved children.

8.2.1 Training Clinicians in Adult Palliative Care to Address the Needs of Children

I remember the first time I was called to go to the adult ICU, working with the six-year-old daughter of a man who had fallen over 50 feet at a construction site. His wife and family were devastated by this tragic event. I was asked to sit with the child while the family met with doctors and discussed the man's life-ending injuries. I recall not knowing what to say or how to respond to her many questions. I am sure I made mistakes, and my interventions would have been greatly improved with academic education, training, and internship. How different this session would have been, had this first experience been mentored and modelled through shadowing an experienced clinician. Mentoring, educating, and supervising clinicians are necessary to advance therapists to meet the needs of grieving and bereaved children.

8.2.2 Systemic Reforms

In sum, medical providers have a responsibility to broaden the understanding of the meaning of patient and family-centred care. Family must include young children and alternative family dynamics. This requires education about the developmental needs of children. Doctors and nurses would need to confront their own biases regarding the inclusion of children. Change could be possible if frontline caregivers recognize ways in which children are excluded. Next steps include in-services, grand rounds presentations, and education about the psychosocial and emotional needs of children as well as funding to create positions to be filled by trained clinicians to provide for the needs of children at the time terminal illnesses affect their closest loved ones.

Here at the end we are not left with stories of death but the lives lived by children, their grief and intention to honour life. A beginning of life on the other side of how we knew it before, and how we live on after the death, a tribute to those we love. Here at the end we are not left with stories of death but the lives lived bychildren, their grief and intention to honour life. A beginning of life on the otherside of how we knew it before, and how we live on after the death, a tribute tothose we love.

A Good Omens Story

References

Association of Child Life Professionals. (n.d.). *History of ACLP*. https://www.childlife.org/about-aclp/news/history-of-aclp

Avis, K. A., Stroebe, M., & Schut, H. (2021). Stages of grief portrayed on the internet: A systematic analysis and critical appraisal. *Frontiers in Psychology, 12*, 1–11.

Berthold, D. (2010). Tidy whiteness: A genealogy of race, purity, and hygiene. *Ethics and the Environment, 15*(1), 1–26. 10.2979/ete.2010.15.1.1

Bettelheim, B. (1976). *The uses of enchantment: The meaning and importance of fairy tales*. Thames & Hudson, UK: Knopf.

Bisconti, T. L., Bergeman, C. S., & Boker, S. M. (2004). Emotional well-being in recently bereaved widows: A dynamical systems approach. *The Journals of Gerontology: Series B, 59*(4), 158–167.

Bowlby, J. (1988). *A secure base: Parent-child attachment and healthy human development*. New York, NY: Basic Books.

Bosmans, G., Bakermans-Kranenburg, M. J., Vervliet, B., Verhees, M. W. F. T., & van Ijzendoorn, M. H. (2020). A learning theory of attachment: Unraveling the black box of attachment development. *Neuroscience & Biobehavioral Reviews, 113*, 287–298.

Carroll, L. (1865). *Alice's adventures in wonderland*. London: Macmillan.

Chabat, A. (Producer), & Balmès, T. (Director). (2010). *Babies [Motion picture]*. France: StudioCanal.

A child's concept of death. (n.d.). Retrieved from Stanford Children's Hospital website: https://www.stanfordchildrens.org/en/topic/default?id=a-childs-concept-of-death-90-P03044

Children's understanding of death at different ages. (n.d.). Retrieved from Child Bereavement UK website: https://www.childbereavementuk.org/information-childrens-understanding-of-death

DiNuzzo, E. (2021, July 21). Here's why we call them "white lies." Reader's Digest. https://www.rd.com/article/why-is-it-called-white-lies/

DK & Smithsonian Institute. (2017). *Knowledge encyclopedia human body!* DK Publication, India: DK Children.

Emunah, R. (1994). *Acting for real: Drama therapy process, technique, and performance*. Brunner/Mazel.

Erikson, E. H. (1950). *Childhood and society* (1st ed.). New York, NY: Norton.

Erikson, E. H. (1959). *Identity and the life cycle*. New York, NY: International Universities Press.

Erikson, E. H. (1968). *Identity, youth and crisis*. New York, NY: Norton.

Fleming, V. (Director). (1939). *The wizard of oz. [Film]*. CA, USA: Metro-Goldwyn-Mayer.

Freud, S. (1962). In Strachey J. (Ed.). *Three essays on the theory of sexuality*. London: Hogarth Press.

Garcia, A., & Buchanan, D. R. (2009). Psychodrama. In D. R. Johnson & R. Emunah (Eds.), *Current approaches in drama therapy* (2nd ed., pp. 393–423). Springfield, IL: Charles C. Thomas.

Gersie, A. (1992). *Storymaking in bereavement: Dragons fight in the meadow*. Philadelphia, PA: Jessica Kingsley.

Hand, R. J., & Wilson, M. (2002). *Grand-Guignol: The French theatre of horror*. Exeter, UK: University of Exeter Press.

Hart, C. L. (2020, October 28). What is a white lie? Psychology Today. https://www.psychologytoday.com/us/blog/the-nature-deception/202010/what-is-white-lie

Homer. (1892). *The odyssey* (G. H. Palmer, Trans.). Boston, USA: Houghton, Mifflin and Company.

Jennings, S. (2011). *Healthy attachments and neuro-dramatic-play*. London: Jessica Kingsley.

Johnson, D. R. (1994). Shame dynamics among creative arts therapies. *The Arts in Psychotherapy*, *21*(3), 173–178.

Johnson, D. R. (2009). Developmental transformations: Toward the body as presence. In D. R. Johnson & R. Emunah (Eds.), *Current approaches in drama therapy* (2nd ed., pp. 87–116). Springfield, IL: Charles C. Thomas.

Johnson, D. R. (2013). *Text for practitioners 2*. New Haven, CT: Institute for Developmental Transformations.

Judi's House/JAG Institute. (2020). https://judishouse.org/wp-content/uploads/2021/10/Judis-House-2020-Impact-Report_Web.pdf

Jung, C. G. (1948). The phenomenology of the spirit in fairy tales. *The Archetypes and the Collective Unconscious*, *9*(1), 207–254.

Kane, S. (1995). *Blasted*. Bloomsbury Publishing PLC, London, UK: Methuen.

Kesselring, J. (1941). *Arsenic and old lace*. Canada: Random House, Inc.

King James Bible. (2017). King James Bible Online. https://www.kingjamesbibleonline.org/ (Original work published 1769)

Koukourikos, K., Tzeha, L., Panteldiou, P., & Tsaloglidou, A. (2015). The importance of play during hospitalization of children. *Mater Sociomed*, *27*(6), 438–441.

Kübler-Ross, E. K. (1969). *On death and dying: What the dying have to teach doctors, nurses, clergy, and their own families*. New York, NY: Touchstone.

Kübler-Ross, E. K., & Kessler, D. (2014). *On grief & grieving: Finding the meaning of grief through the five stages of loss*. New York, USA: Scribner.

Landy, R. J. (2007). *Persona and performance: The meaning of role in drama, therapy, and everyday life*. London: Jessica Kingsley.

Lasseter, J. (Director). (1995). *Toy story. [Film]*. Walt Disney Studios Motion Pictures.

Lasseter, J. (Director). (1999). *Toy story 2. [Film]*. Walt Disney Studios Motion Pictures.

Leeuwenburgh, E., & Goldring, E. (2008). *Why did you die?* Oakland, CA:New Harbinger.

Levine, P. A. (1997). *Waking the tiger: Healing trauma*. Berkeley, CA: North Atlantic Books.

Maslow, A. H. (1970). *Motivation and personality* (2nd ed.). New York, USA: Harper & Row.

Menakem, R. (2017). *My grandmother's hands: racialized trauma and the pathway to mending our hearts and bodies*. Las Vegas, NV: Central Recovery Press.

Miller, A. (1952). *The crucible*. New York, USA: Viking Penguin Inc.

Mount, A. (2022, September 26). The "golden hour": Giving your newborn the best start. Sanford Health. https://news.sanfordhealth.org/womens/pregnancy/the-golden-hour-giving-your-newborn-the-best-start/

National Consensus Project for Quality Palliative Care. (2018). *Clinical practice guidelines for quality palliative care* (4th ed.). Virginia, USA: National Coalition for Hospice and Palliative Care.

North American Drama Therapy Association. (2017). *NADTA scope of practice*. https://www.nadta.org/about-nadta/scope-of-practice.html

Omens, S. (2014). Body as impasse: Drama therapy with medically compromised children. In N. Sajnani & D. R. Johnson (Eds.), *Trauma informed drama therapy: Transforming clinics, classrooms, and communities* (pp. 270–286). Springfield: Charles C Thomas.

Omens, S. (2017). *About the baby (W. Gunn, Illus.)*. New York, NY: No White Lies.

Omens, S. (2017). *Cancer changes (W. Gunn, Illus.)*. New York, NY: No White Lies.

Omens, S. (2017). *Everything changes (W. Gunn, Illus.)*. New York, NY: No White Lies.

Penn, A. (1993). *The kissing hand* (N. M. Leak & R. E. Harper, Illus.). Washington, DC: Child Welfare League of America.

Perlman, M. (2018, March 5). The true origins of "white lies." Columbia Journalism Review. https://www.cjr.org/language_corner/white-lies-hope-hicks.php

Peterson, L. (1989). Coping by children undergoing stressful medical procedures: Some conceptual, methodological, and therapeutic issues. *Journal of Consulting and Clinical Psychology, 57*(3), 380–387. 10.1037/0022-006X.57.3.380

Piaget, J. (1952). *The origins of intelligence in children* (M. T. Cook, Trans.). New York, NY: International University Press.

Reiner, R. (Director). (1992).*A few good men. [Film]*. Columbia Pictures.

Romito, B., Jewell, J., Jackson, M., & AAP Committee on Hospital Care; Association of Child Life Professionals. (2020). Child life services. *Pediatrics, 146*(6), 1–10. 10.1542/peds.2020-040261

Salek, E. C., & Ginsburg, K. R. (2014). *How children understand death & what you should say*. Retrieved from American Academy of Pediatrics: https://healthychildren.org/English/healthy-living/emotional-wellness/Building-Resilience/Pages/How-Children-Understand-Death-What-You-Should-Say.aspx

Seuss, Dr. (1954). *Horton hears a who*. New York, NY: Random House.

Shakespeare, W. (2003). *Macbeth*. New York, NY: Simon & Schuster. (Original work published 1623).

Shakespeare, W. (2005). *Titus Andronicus*. New York, NY: Simon & Schuster. (Original work published 1594).

Shakespeare, W. (2011). A midsummer night's dream. In R. Proudfoot, A. Thompson, & D. S. Kastan (Eds.), *The Arden complete Shakespeare works* (Rev. ed., pp. 889–913). London, UK: Methuen Drama. (Original work published 1600).

Shakespeare, W. (2011). *As you like it*. In R. Proudfoot, A. Thompson, & D. S. Kastan (Eds.), *The Arden complete Shakespeare works* (Rev. ed., pp. 161–191). London, UK: Methuen Drama. (Original work published 1623).

Sherman, G. D., & Clore, G. L. (2009). The color of sin: White and black are perceptual symbols of moral purity and pollution. *Psychological Science, 20*(8), 1019–1025. 10.1111/j.1467-9280.2009.02403.x

Sophocles. (2005). *Oedipus rex* (J. E. Thomas, Trans.). Georgia, USA: Prestwick House. (Original work published 420 B.C.E).

Spolin, V. (1999). *Improvisation for the theater: A handbook of teaching and directing techniques* (3rd ed.). Evanston, IL: Northwestern University Press.

Stroebe, M., Schut, H., & Boerner, K. (2017). Cautioning health-care professionals: Bereaved persons are misguided through the stages of grief. *OMEGA – Journal of Death and Dying, 74*(4), 455–473. 10.1177/0030222817691870

The theater: Murders in the Rue Chaptal. (1947, March 10). *Time.* https://content.time.com/time/subscriber/article/0,33009,886404,00.html

Van der Kolk, B. A. (2014). *The body keeps the score: Brain, mind, and body in the healing of trauma.* New York, NY: Penguin Books.

Vygotsky, L. S. (1967). Play and its role in the mental development of the child. *Soviet Psychology, 5,* 6–18.

Wilder, T. (2020). *Our town.* New York, NY: Harper Perennial Modern Classics. (Original work published 1938).

Winnicott, D. W. (1960). The theory of the parent-infant relationship. *International Journal of Psychoanalysis, 41,* 585–595.

Winnicott, D. W. (2005). *Playing and reality.* New York, NY: Routledge Classics. (Original work published 1971).

Wynne, A. (1932).*All through the year: Three hundred and sixty-five new poems for holidays and every day.* New York, NY: Frederick A. Stokes Company.

Tucker, Z. B. (2021). *Understanding the human body: Anatomy made easy for kids.* (n.p.).

Index